THE BANKNOTE YEARBOOK

THE
BANKNOTE
YEARBOOK
2002

Edited by
James Mackay, MA, DLitt
John W. Mussell
and
the Editorial Team of BANKNOTE NEWS

Consultant Editor
Pam West

ISBN 1 870 192 45 1

Published by
TOKEN PUBLISHING LIMITED
Orchard House, Heathpark, Honiton, Devon EX14 1YD, UK
Telephone: 01404 46972   Fax: 01404 44788
e-mail: info@tokenpublishing.com   Website: www.tokenpublishing.com

CONTENTS

INDEX TO ADVERTISERS

THE DOUBLE SOVEREIGN

2001

BANK NOTES
OF THE DARK
CONTINENT

AN ALTERNATIVE TO AUCTIONS

With the Major U.K. Auctions now charging
15% to the vendor and 15% to the buyer (plus V.A.T. on commission)
it is now financially prohibitive for collectors to sell coins by public auction.

We can now offer an alternative !!!

We will sell your collection through our Double Sovereign magazine and charge you a flat fee of 1

The advantage for you is that all the coins will be sold to collectors world
wide so you will get a full retail price minus 10%. Our magazine
reaches 6500 people worldwide who buy coins,
medals and banknotes.

We also buy English and World Bank Notes
If you are interested in this
service please contact David Ilsley
01525 383822

22 HIGH STREET
LEIGHTON BUZZARD
BEDS LU7 1EA UNITED KINGDOM

DOLPHIN COINS
AND MEDALS
LTD
ESTABLISHED 1967

TEL: 01525 383
FAX: 01525 383
WEB SITE: WWW.DOLPHINCOINS.C

PREFACE

IT was with some trepidation that we decided to go ahead last year with the first edition of the BANKNOTE YEARBOOK, but not only have we had immensely encouraging feedback from readers, but the first edition was almost completely sold out within a few months. We had hoped to launch a separate periodical for collectors of paper money but sheer pressure of other commitments over the past twelve months has prevented us from realising this ambition and for the moment, therefore, features on paper money as well as news and new issues are provided in the banknote section of COIN NEWS.

The core of this yearbook is the price guide to British banknotes. We have endeavoured to expand this section but more importantly the prices have been completely revised and up-dated in line with the latest market prices and auction realisations. Plans are already in hand to expand the listing of notes still further. We are fully cognisant of the fact that there are much more detailed catalogues and monographs dealing with all aspects of banking history as well as the issues of specific banks, but we are responding to a deeply felt need for the salient information distilled into a single manageable volume, hence the tried and tested formula which we had previously adopted in the sister publication COIN YEARBOOK.

In the previous edition we included a survey of the important events and happenings in the paper money world over a period of about eighteen months; in this edition we have confined our review to the past twelve months and this brings this reference work into line with COIN YEARBOOK and MEDAL YEARBOOK.

The past year has been a remarkably buoyant one for the hobby of notaphily, with some spectacular results at auction. More importantly dealers report a significant increase in the level of interest with many new collectors taking up the hobby.

At the time of writing we are poised on the brink of the greatest monetary upheaval since Roman times, as twelve of the fifteen member countries of the European Union embrace the euro and abandon their centuries old national currency systems. There has been widespread interest, in and out of the EU, regarding the forthcoming changes and we feel that this can only help to further stimulate interest. There has also been intense speculation regarding the disposal of the billions of banknotes which will become redundant in the coming months, and it is to be hoped that a fair proportion of this material will be made available to the numismatic market.

This promises to be an interesting period for collateral material, such as the propaganda leaflets being distributed to the general public in the relevant countries. Do not overlook the potential of collectables in related fields such as stamps and postmarks, coins and medals which herald the Euro or say farewell to the outgoing currencies.

If the United Kingdom eventually comes into line and embraces the Euro, will this mean the end of the notes not only of the Bank of England but also the three Scottish banks? All four institutions have been very active in the past year, with new notes in general circulation and, more particularly, commemoratives. Last year we referred to the special Bank of England £10 note with the prefix celebrating the hundredth birthday of the Queen Mother, but subsequently the Royal Bank of Scotland issued a wholly distinctive note for the same happy event, and it is expected that one or more of the British banks will produce special notes to celebrate the Queen's Golden Jubilee.

While the notes of the European Central Bank will probably provide some scope for the collector looking for a fresh field to study, the obsolescent notes of the EU countries will continue to attract attention for the foreseeable future. Farther afield, of course, the new countries of eastern and central Europe will, we are sure, generate considerable interest; a significant proportion of the new issues chronicled by the London Banknote Monetary Research Centre in the Banknote News section of COIN NEWS in the past year has emanated from the successor states of the former Soviet Union and Yugoslavia, and although these have included some rather controversial issues from Kosovo and Transdniestria there is no doubt that such notes possess immense historical interest.

In producing a volume such as this we have had to call on a number of experts for assistance. Our grateful thanks are extended to everyone who has helped make this publication not only possible but also establish it as the authoritative reference work for collectors and students of British banknotes. In particular we wish to thank Pam West, our consultant editor and well-known paper money dealer who as well as helping to check the proofs, has also generously provided a number of notes for illustration. Thanks are also due to Trevor Jones of Banking Memorabilia, and to Mártan Mac Devitt for allowing us to reproduce illustrations from *20th Century Scottish Banknotes* and *Irish Banknotes, Irish Government Paper Money From 1928*, respectively, the standard works on the subjects, also to the London Banknote Monetary Research Centre for providing a number of illustrations. A number of private collectors have supplied us with corrections as well as useful illustrations while Michael Brill, Tim Lawes, Chris Leadston, Mártan Mac Devitt, Gordon McLoughlin, David Murphy and Michael O'Grady, have proffered much professional advice and assistance with the catalogue section. We also owe a debt of gratitude to the authors and publishers of various specialist books that have enabled us to check the data included in this important section. We wholeheartedly recommend readers who wish to pursue the hobby seriously to consult the works listed in the Bibliography.

That was
THE YEAR
that was!

An at-a-glance résumé of the main events and occurrences that affected banknotes and paper money during the past months, as reported in Banknote News, the note section of COIN NEWS.

April 2000

Photo courtesy The Bank of England.

John Fforde, the man who signed the Bank of England notes from 1966 to 1970, dies on April 10 aged 78. Born in 1921, his education at Rossall School was interrupted by the War and he joined the RAF. After the War he read philosophy, politics and economics at Christ Church College, Oxford. He continued his education at Nuffield College where he wrote his doctoral thesis on the Federal Reserve System, 1945–9. He joined the Bank in 1956 as an economic adviser and in 1959 became deputy chief of the economic intelligence department. He was appointed Chief Cashier in 1966. Although he signed the banknotes, this position was then akin to being the Bank's chief executive officer. He was an executive director of the Bank from 1970 to 1982 and Advisor to the Governor in 1982–4. On retirement he was appointed the Bank's official historian and as a result he published *The Bank of England and Public Policy 1941–58*.

May 2000

The Chatham Islands, famous as being the place where the first sunrise of the new Millennium took place, subsequently celebrates the occasion by releasing its very first issue of paper money. The Millennium First Notes comprise $2, $3, $10 and $15 denominations, traded as negotiable tender on the islands which normally use New Zealand currency. Issued by authority of the Chatham Islands Note Corporation, they are on par with the NZ dollar. Printed on non-tear, high-density polyethylene, the notes depict island birds on the obverse and scenic vignettes on the reverse.

June 2000

An exhibition at the Bank of England, open until October 5, gives a fascinating insight into contemporary views of the Bank through the many cartoons and caricatures published from the 18th century to the present day.

August 2000

The hundredth birthday of Her Majesty Queen Elizabeth the Queen Mother is celebrated on August 4 with the release of a special envelope franked with the Windsor

Castle £5 stamp and containing the £5 cupro-nickel crown and a Bank of England £5 note with the prefix QM 100. This is the first time that a banknote has been issued with a Q prefix. Only 10,000 covers were produced to retail at £49.95. This exotic souvenir was the result of collaboration between Debden Security Printing and the Royal Mint.

September 2000

The Paper Money Show, organised by Quentin Frères, takes place on September 24 at the Hotel Ibis, Porte de Clichy.

October 2000

Phillips, the London auctioneers, hold a major sale of paper money on October 5, while Spink have a large note section in their sale the following day. A highlight of the Spink sale is one of the earliest recorded Bank of England £100 notes, discovered by the vendor in an old piece of furniture. It is knocked down for £35,000, more than twice the pre-sale estimate. The sale realised £540,000, a record for a UK paper money sale.

The early £100 note sold at Spink on October 5, 2000.

Both of the banknote auctions in October were as attractive curtain raisers for the World Paper Money Fair which takes place over the weekend of October 7–8 at the Trades Union Congress Centre in London. Over 100 major dealers take part. This 30th annual event is organised by the London Chapter of the International Bank Note Society.

The annual convention of the Australian Chapter of the International Bank Note Society is held in Sydney over the weekend of October 7–8. Despite the clash of dates in the two major world events, the Australian convention draws a large turn-out of international dealers and visitors.

The Royal Mint collaborates with Debden Security Printing in the production of a special Millennium souvenir pack, incorporating an Elgar £20 note and a Millennium silver proof coin. The notes have the special prefix Y20 and serial numbers between 000395 and 002000.

Detail of the newly-designed £10 note.

November 2000

Cashiers at the Bank of England's main branch in Threadneedle Street are astounded to find a queue outside the front door on November 7, the day that the Charles Darwin £10 note is launched. The notes, signed by Ms Merlyn Lowther, replace the notes portraying Charles Dickens. Both men were heavily bearded, a feature much prized as a security device because it is difficult to replicate the fine detail in facial hair.

The Iraqi government announces plans to dispense with the US dollar in settling accounts, the greenback being denounced as "manipulated by International Zionism and American interests". There is speculation that Iraq may use the Euro instead. Meanwhile currency dealers in Iraq continue to use US currency, as the highest Iraqi denomination, the 250 dinar note, is only worth about 10 cents.

February 2001

The London Paper Money Fair takes place at the Bonnington Hotel on February 4, the day following the London Coin Fair at the Cumberland Hotel.

The well-known German paper money dealer, Holger Rosenberg, dies after a long illness. He had carried on a business that had been founded by his father and although he sold the business in 1998 owing to ill health his demise comes as a shock to collectors and dealers around the world.

March 2001

The French police issue a warning that forged 500 franc notes have begun to turn up in circulation. The forgeries are believed to be excellent, but lack the variable optical effect in the UV imprint.

Examples of the new Darwin £10 note are reported in circulation without the special security "silver" thread. At first regarded as counterfeit, they subsequently prove to be quite genuine and thus constitute a major collectable variety.

The Bank of England withdraws the Michael Faraday £20 note after a decade in use and replaces it with the note portraying Sir Edward Elgar.

The Clydesdale Bank of Scotland reveals plans to issue new £50 and £100 notes celebrating the 550th anniversary of Glasgow University, the fourth oldest university in Britain (after Oxford, Cambridge and St Andrews). The notes have the prefix GU and include the distinctive anniversary logo. They are also the first Clydesdale notes to bear the signature of the new Chief Executive, Stuart Grimshaw.

Mel Steinberg and customers at the Maastricht Fair.

April 2001

The European Papermoney Bourse, popularly known as the Maastricht Fair, takes place in the Geulhal in Valkenburg on the outskirts of Maastricht over the weekend of April 7–8.

May 2001

"Forgery, the Artful Crime" is the title of an exhibition which opens at the Bank of England Museum. It traces the history of counterfeiting Bank of England notes over a period of three centuries, and the various preventive measures taken to combat this crime.

The latest bank to go plastic is the Banco de Mexico which launches an experimental 20 peso note in polymer. At the same time, the bank announces plans to improve the quality of the high-value notes with enhanced security devices and optically variable ink.

Spink hold a major paper money sale on May 3. Almost 1,000 lots go under the hammer, and include a fascinating old collection of Bank of England notes which had not been seen for many years and was therefore new to the market. Other highlights include a strong Scottish section and a specialised study of the notes of Mauritius.

19th century broadsheet from the Bank of England Museum's exhibition on forgery through the ages.

The London Paper Money Fair takes place at the Bonnington Hotel on May 6.

Plans to defeat the forger are revealed and include a new advanced micro-optical character recognition device which will shut down computers and photocopiers if any attempt is made to scan or copy notes. Already, manufacturers of photocopiers are incorporating features in their machines which will defeat the would-be counterfeiter.

The London Chapter of the IBNS hold a mini-bourse and social gathering at the Victory Services Club, Marble Arch on May 31.

June 2001

The London Coin Fair takes place in the Cumberland Hotel at Marble Arch on June 23 for the last time prior to its move to the Holiday Inn in Bloomsbury.

Frances Simmon s, organiser of the London Coin Fairs.

The Czech Republic demonetises the 1993 series of 1000 and 5000 crown notes on June 30. They had been superseded by notes in 1996 and 1999, superficially similar in design but with improved security devices and a graphic motif on the reverse.

The Royal Mint is appointed to sell the collector products hitherto marketed by Britannia Giftware, a division of Debden Security Printing Limited. The entire range of banknote sets and related items which have been distributed by Debden since 1990 will now be handled by the Royal Mint in addition to its own range of coins and medals.

July 2001

At a Warwick and Warwick sale on July 11 a specimen printing of a 1924 Chinese $50 note of the Bank of South East Asia, estimated at £20, is knocked down for £775.

The printing plate used at Mafeking to produce the distinctive notes during the siege of 1900 during the Anglo-Boer war comes under the hammer at an auction held by City Coins (South Africa) on July 13. The siege notes, now very rare and valuable, were the brainchild of the beleaguered town's commander, Colonel Robert Baden-Powell who founded the Boy Scout movement seven years later.

August 2001

The American Bank Note Company denounces the latest move by the Bureau of Engraving and Printing which is seeking permission from Congress to print banknotes for countries other than the USA. ABNC believe that the entry of BEP into the fiercely competitive international commercial market would give the Bureau an unfair advantage, being an organisation controlled and funded by the federal government.

September 2001

The London Paper Money Fair is held at the Bonnington Hotel, Southampton Row on September 2.

The European Central Bank releases final details regarding the Euro notes which go into circulation in the EU countries which have agreed to the single currency. From January 2002 the Euro replaces the Deutschemark, the franc, the peseta, the lira and all the other national currencies of the twelve countries which have agreed to the most important monetary union in the entire history of money.

Sibil, the international banknote fair organised by the Quentin brothers of Paris takes place on September 23 at the Ibis Hotel, avenue de Clichy.

October 2001

The 31st annual World Paper Money Fair, the oldest event of its kind in the world, is held at the Trades Union Congress Centre, Great Russell Street, London over the weekend of October 6–7, under the sponsorship of the London Chapter of the International Banknote Society. Both Spink and Phillips hold auctions to coincide with the event.

The Best and worst
of recent banknote designs

The period under review (the latter part of 2000 and the first half of 2001) was memorable for a number of Millennium related issues around the world. The Bank of England introduced new designs in the £10 and £20 notes, while, north of the border, the Clydesdale Bank proved to be the most innovative of the three Scottish banks, with £50 and £100 notes marking the 550th anniversary of Glasgow University. Although eyebrows were raised at the last-named, on account of its high face value, this denomination was an obvious choice since it has depicted the neo-Gothic pile of the University on the reverse ever since this denomination was added to the present series. Not to be outdone, the Royal Bank of Scotland produced a £20 note to celebrate the Queen Mother's hundredth birthday, the charming reverse showing a recent portrait of Her Majesty, along with a picture of her as a little girl, her ancestral home at Glamis Castle and a bouquet of Elizabeth of Glamis roses. Apart from the happy occasion which inspired this issue, it must surely rank high as one of the most attractive notes of the past year.

It has been a momentous year in many parts of the world. Greater stability in the economies of the successor states of the Soviet Union and Yugoslavia has been reflected in the release of new notes in many of them, a far cry aesthetically and technically from the relatively crude makeshifts of the previous decade. And over all loomed the most momentous change of all, the introduction of the Euro at the beginning of 2002, when the distinctive currencies of the EU countries that have signed up for the single currency are taken out of circulation. There was considerable speculation in the lay press regarding the obsolete notes and it was hoped that some at least would be made available to the collector market and thereby stimulate a further growth in notaphily.

Although the currency in most countries was more stable than at any other time in the past 20 years, the trend towards the replacement of notes by coins continued, with a corresponding introduction of new notes of even higher face value than before. Among countries which upgraded their paper money in this way were Belarus (10,000 roubles), Colombia (50,000 pesos), Hungary (20,000 forint), Mozambique (200,000 meticals), Romania (500,000 lei), Russia (1,000 new roubles) and Venezuela (20,000 and 50,000 bolivares). Information on the current position in Turkey is not available but with the cost of sending an aerogramme now in excess of a million lire one shudders to think what astronomical denominations are now in use.

The Royal Bank of Scotland's £20 note to celebrate the Queen Mother's 100th birthday.

An entirely new series of notes was introduced in Liberia as a result of the formation of the Central Bank in place of the former National Bank, The creation of the new bank was politically motivated, in a bid to restore unity to a country torn apart by civil wars. A desire to wipe the slate clean and heal wounds at home and abroad likewise lay behind the decision of Yugoslavia to embark on an entirely new series of dinars, now that the Milosevic era was at an end. The rouble was replaced by distinctive national currencies in several parts of the former USSR, notably the somoni of Tajikistan and the som of the neighbouring Kyrgyz Republic.

The Kyrgyz Republic's 200 som banknote released on August 28, 2000.

Further changes reflected the increasing problems of defeating the counterfeiter and beating the technology now available to the criminal fraternity. While forgery was combated on one level by installing programs in computers and photocopiers which would shut them down if illegal scanning was attempted, banks and governments continued to look for ways of enhancing the security of their notes, with metal threads, holograms, micro-lettering, latent imaging and variably optical inks. Others sought to make their notes more durable by resorting to various plastic substances, but considering that tyvek and other polymers have been around for 20 years it is surprising that more use has not been made of these hard-wearing, non-tear materials. Embossed or raised surfaces in various patterns have become more common as issuing authorities recognise the problems faced by the visually impaired in distinguishing the values of notes.

But what of the actual designs that have emerged over the past twelve months? It has been very much a case of the mixture as before, with most countries relying on a tried and tested formula. It is significant that the USA has persevered with the $1 and $5 notes in the old pattern portraying Washington and Lincoln (even though these notes now have a very short life in circulation and ought to have been replaced by coins long ago), while the revamped designs of the higher denominations—retaining the same portrait gallery even if the actual portraits have been updated—have come in for

a great deal of criticism, for no good reason at all, other than that the opportunity has been taken in recent years to modernise the designs by removing the vegetation in the borders. The plain fact of the matter is that the general public in every country is essentially conservative in outlook, especially where its banknotes are concerned. One suspects that the increase in the size of the portraits of American notes has been dictated by security reasons, for the human eye instinctively detects the slightest change in a person's appearance—a point which has often tripped up the counterfeiter.

Portraiture continued to dominate new banknote designs during the past year. While the USA has been content to stick to the same old gallery of dead presidents, every other country seems intent on finding new faces. I suspect that this is designed to acquaint the public with the great and the good of the past, for many of the celebrities thus honoured are little known outside their native land (and sometimes not too well known inside it either). Who knows anything about the gent on Venezuela's 20,000 bolivares, with the specs perched on his forehead? Simon Rodriguez (1769–1854) was apparently known as the Socrates of Colombia although his chief claim to fame seems to be that he once tutored Simon Bolivar.

Since 1998 Armenia has been issuing notes portraying famous Armenians. This must be even more difficult than the old game of naming ten famous Belgians, for the resultant celebrities appear to be virtually unknown beyond the Caucasus. Hovhannes Tumanyan, whose bearded face stares out of the new 5000 dram note, was allegedly the most famous Armenian writer at the beginning of the 20th century, but you might be hard pressed to find his entry in most biographical dictionaries.

Armenia's Tumanyan on the new 500 dram.

Sheik Mujibur Rahman (Bangladesh) and Sir Ahmadu Bello (Nigeria) are good examples of political figures who will always be remembered in their native countries for their role in shaping them or striving for their independence, but

Kapitan Pattimura (Indonesia) is an enigma. As for the personalities who adorn the new somoni notes of Tajikistan, we are even further hampered by the fact that their names are not rendered in a script that is intelligible beyond the Tajik frontiers. Sometimes we get a clue to the identity of the portrait, from the details on the reverse of a note. Thus the new 1 som from the Kyrgyz Republic has a reverse motif of musical instruments and the State Concert Hall in Bishkek (but of course, where else?) which allude to the portrait of Abdylas Maldybaev, a singer of great repute. Going over the portraits notes of the past year, however, I find that the great majority of them do not include even a brief caption naming the personality, far less supplying details of profession and dates of birth and death, and even when such details are given they tend to be so minuscule as to be barely legible. May I therefore make a plea to banknote printers and designers to give greater prominence to such information.

Apart from portraiture the preferred subject at the moment is architecture, ranging from past glories to ultra-modern public works. Indeed, this has now become so prevalent that a notaphilist who was also an architect could probably form a very interesting collection on that basis alone, perhaps matching the vignettes with actual photographs to contrast reality with the modifications required to make the motif fit in with the exigencies of layout, inscription and dimensions.

Scenery, which once dominated the backs of notes, is not so much in evidence these days, although the past year has yielded several notable examples of the genre, such as the placid lake scene on the back of China's 20 yuan, or the view of Issyk-Kul Lake on the back of the 200 som from the Kyrgyz Republic. Other themes have only found fleeting reference. Surinam alone has produced a new series with a unified theme (birds), but otherwise this once popular theme has had short shrift, though I rather like Romania's new 500,000 lei note which shows a mountain eagle alongside one of the early monoplanes built by Aurel Vlaicu whose portrait graces the obverse.

There seem to be two distinct schools of thought in banknote design. On the one hand there is the minimalist style which completely eschews frames and borders and avoids extraneous ornament. Superficially a large proportion of both back and front are blank, although generally speaking this serves to highlight such security devices as watermarks and special paper. Recent examples of this include the 10 latu of Latvia, the Mao portrait series of China and the latest issues from

Australia's $5 note celebrating the Centenary of Federation, featuring Sir Henry Parkes and Catherine Helen Spence.

Colombia, Russia, Belarus and Transdniestria. The latest notes from the Faroe Islands have taken this principle a stage further, the motifs themselves being minimalist and devoid of any explanatory text. The 50 kronur is, quite frankly, baffling and compares unfavourably with its Danish counterpart which circulates alongside.

At the other end of the spectrum are notes which have an overall pattern or motif, extending to the edges of the paper on one or both sides. The prime example of this is the new series from Suriname, the reverses of whose notes are a riot of colour which enhances rather than detracts from the principal motifs of exotic birds. The Gandhi series of India is in the same genre, although it has a circular watermark panel for good measure. Armenia, Mozambique and Romania all have new notes with printing bled off at the edges.

Last year I commented that, apart from the Scottish banks, commemorative notes were few and far between. This has continued to be the case over the period under review. Hungary released a 2000 forint which neatly linked 1000 years of nationhood to 2000 years of Christianity in the person of St Stephen whose crown was featured on the obverse. The centennial of the Commonwealth of Australia was celebrated by a new $5 note portraying Sir Henry Parkes, the "Father of Confederation" and Helen Spence, the journalist, feminist, social reformer and first lady of Australian politics. Armenia celebrated 1700 years of Christianity with a 50,000 dram note, but as this is now the highest denomination in circulation it seems probable that this is intended for general circulation for the foreseeable future, rather than a temporary issue.

Notaphily
the hobby

Notaphily, the hobby of collecting paper money, is of relatively recent growth. The name for the hobby was invented as recently as 1969 and is not entirely satisfactory since it is partly from the Latin—*nota* (a note) and the Greek—*philos* (love), when it should preferably have been derived from the same language. That collectors should only have got around to coining an expression for their hobby within the past three decades or so is an indication of its very recent development. Yet there is evidence to suggest that paper money was being collected more than two centuries ago, for printed sheets of different *assignats* and *mandats* were produced as souvenirs and must have catered to people who were interested in them as historical documents of the French Revolution, rather than as actual spending money.

It is really only since World War I that paper money has been universally accepted in place of silver and gold and thus it is within the past three quarters of a century that notaphily has become popular. Many of the notes of the broken banks, or the paper money produced in times of economic upheaval, were only preserved by chance or by people who laid aside specimens as curiosities.

There was no market for obsolete paper money until fairly recently and notes were seldom acquired in large quantities for distribution to dealers and collectors. At the same time, apart from a few eccentric characters who collected paper money, collectors were few and far between, until after World War I. Some fantastically large collections of banknotes were formed in the nineteenth century and formed the nucleus of our present-day knowledge of the subject. Ludwig Clericus of Magdeburg, for example, began collecting paper money in the 1870s. Clericus wrote several important books and many articles about paper money. After his death the German State Printing Works in Berlin purchased his collection but unfortunately it was destroyed in the bombing of Berlin in 1945. Most of the great nineteenth and early twentieth century collections were formed in Germany or Austria and many of them suffered great losses during the two world wars. The Pflumer collection, amounting to over 10,000 items, was purchased by the Marquess of Bute, who was also noted for his collection of airmail and war stamps, and these collections suffered heavy loss when the London home of the Marquess was destroyed during the London Blitz.

Notaphily received its first great stimulus during and after World War I with the appearance of the high-denomination German banknotes and the myriads of *Notgeld*. For the first time the hobby captured

Examples of Notgeld.

Japanese Invasion Money—commonly referred to as "JIM" notes.

the imagination of the man in the street as well as the wealthy scholar or historian. Interest waned in the 1930s, but rose again during and after World War II and a new generation of collectors was recruited to the hobby by the vast quantities of Japanese occupation currency which flooded Europe and America after the war. As coin and medal collecting boomed in popularity in the 1960s so also did paper money collecting. Hitherto collectors had little opportunity to purchase examples of paper money. Occasionally coin dealers would include a few banknotes in their stock but, generally speaking, they took little interest in this aspect of numismatics and knowledgeable collectors could often pick up rare items for a fraction of their true value. Now there are many important dealers who specialise in paper money and publish detailed catalogues and price lists.

Numismatic magazines on both sides of the Atlantic now give a great deal of space to

COIN NEWS, Britain's biggest selling coin magazine includes a BANKNOTE NEWS section every month. To subscribe call 01404 44166, fax 01404 44788 or visit: www.tokenpublishing.com for a free sample.

features on paper money and carry extensive advertising from dealers who specialise in this field. Collecting is made easier, especially for the beginner, by the attractive packets of mixed notes on offer. Packs of obsolete banknotes have also been given away as premium offers by manufacturers of many different commodities, from cigarettes to shampoo. By saving two or more packets or labels from the appropriate brand, the would-be collector could send off to the manufacturer and receive, in return, a bundle of attractive banknotes with which to start off his collection. In recent years there have also been several offers of a similar nature associated with newspaper or magazine promotions.

The traditional methods of acquiring new material should not be overlooked. Sixty years ago, before World War II, when there were no currency restrictions, banks and travel agents were a happy hunting ground for the banknote collector and attractive and unusual specimens of notes from all over the world could be obtained in this way, merely by paying the going exchange rates. There was a time when a friendly local bank manager, especially in a country like Scotland where many different notes were in circulation, might be prevailed upon to keep an eye out for rare or unusual specimens. I recall a bank manager in the Western Isles, during a wartime fund-raising campaign, receiving a bundle of notes of the City of Glasgow Bank which had crashed spectacularly in 1879. The notes had been lovingly hoarded for more than sixty years by some crofter, unaware that they had ceased to have any real monetary value, although their numismatic value must have been not inconsiderable.

Taxi-drivers, hoteliers and shopkeepers, especially those catering largely to tourists and foreign visitors, were another fertile source of collectable banknotes from far and wide. Even nowadays, when money has been largely superseded by credit cards, foreign notes are sometimes proffered in payment of relatively small amounts. Conversely, foreign travel by friends and family can often yield interesting examples of paper money. Servicemen in both world wars as well as a host of minor campaigns often had unrivalled opportunities to secure paper money in large quantities, especially in cases where the paper money has become worthless on account of the downfall of a government or the surrender of a country, as happened with Germany in 1918 and 1945.

Examples of old paper money turn up in the oddest places. Distrust of banks has led many a canny individual to salt away his or her money in the upholstery of furniture or a mattress and little caches of banknotes have often come to light when old bedding and furniture was being broken up. Banknotes have been used as bookmarks by absent-minded individuals, turning up many years later, perhaps when the books were cleared out and sold to a dealer. Antique dealers have sometimes found bundles of old banknotes secreted in the drawers of desks and bureaux and, if the original owner cannot be traced, these notes invariably come into the hands of collectors. Examples of the siege notes from Mafeking and the picturesque notes of the Confederate States have been known to turn up in contemporary correspondence, acquired as curiosities at the time but long-forgotten until brought to light many years after the event. Until the advent of banknote dealers, the search for old paper money added a great deal of zest and excitement to the hobby. Even now, part of the fun of collecting banknotes can lie in the unusual manner in which the prize specimens were obtained.

Top: A Mafeking siege note. Below: A Confederate States of America $100 note from the Montgomery issue 1861.

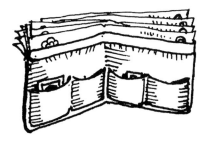

A guide to
Condition

Condition of Paper Money

Before the hobby got properly organised many collectors were quite happy to give house room to notes whose condition was far from perfect. The justification for this was that, since paper money was seldom if ever laid aside at the time of issue for preservation in a collection, it was bound to show some signs of wear and tear through having been passed from hand to hand. Thus blemishes such as creases, pin-holes and dog-eared corners were usually disregarded. In many cases, so few examples of a particular note had been preserved at all that collectors were glad to have them in any condition; half a note was better than none at all.

With the development of the hobby and the hardening of the market, however, the old free and easy approach to condition began to disappear. Many notes now pass straight from the banks into the hands of notaphilists and are preserved in impeccable condition. Furthermore a large proportion of the obsolete notes are now turning up in better condition than ever, as interest in collecting develops and people search out items which had been hidden away. Consequently, as dealers' price lists developed into standard catalogues, condition became an increasingly important factor in determining the value of banknotes and other forms of paper money. Generally the market in 19th century or earlier notes (where they are available) is not so dependent on condition as later notes.

Nevertheless, perfection will not always be possible. When compared to other collectable objects, paper money comes off rather badly. Banknotes are made of paper, as are postage stamps, but are expected to endure infinitely rougher usage. They have to perform the same function as coins, without being of the same hard-wearing materials. So used banknotes will always have a place in a paper money collection, although the collector should try always to obtain the finest examples he can find.

There are five factors which affect the condition, and therefore the value, of a banknote. The first of these is cleanliness. The ideal banknote should have a fresh appearance, without dirty or unsightly finger marks. Slight dirt marks, dust marks or light staining would make it less desirable, but still quite presentable. The value of a note would drop very sharply if it was very dirty, or was disfigured by those squiggles which bank clerks delight in making with ball-point pens or indelible pencils. Very grubby notes would only be worth preserving as space fillers, until better specimens were obtainable.

Although very dirty notes *can* be cleaned, this is not generally recommended except for common or cheap notes, as cleaning will detract from the value of a note.

The second factor is creasing. A banknote which has been folded in half, but is otherwise in clean, fresh condition, would still be a desirable item. One or two folds of this sort would not make much difference to the value of a note, but where it has been folded a number of times, both horizontally and vertically, it would not be such an attractive item. Prolonged folding produces heavy creases which may actually damage the surface of the note, and in these cases it would have to be regarded merely as a space filler until a note of a higher grade can replace it.

Surface damage is the third factor to take into account. The mildest form of surface damage would consist of crumpling, but it is surprising what pressure between the pages of a book can do! Other forms of damage include severe staining, rubbing, rust marks, foxing (caused by iron impurities in the paper reacting with the humidity of the atmosphere), scratches, thinning or tears, and as the damage becomes progressively worse so the value of the note diminishes.

The edges of a banknote are prone to damage and this constitutes the fourth factor. Slight nicks in the edges of a banknote or minute creasing across the corners would not have much adverse effect on its value, but extensive tears or chunks of paper actually missing round the edges would not be desirable. If the corners were heavily dog-eared, or one or more corners were actually missing, the note would again have no more than "space filler" value.

Damage to the body of the note is the fifth factor. Under this heading come pin-holes, slight tears or rusting caused by staples or paper clips, or any other kind of damage resulting in holes or tears in the note itself. In extreme cases notes may actually have been torn or cut in half and subsequently repaired with sticky tape. Here again, the advisability of retaining such specimens for the collection would depend largely on whether better examples are likely to turn up or not. Adhesive tape, such as Sellotape or Scotch tape, may be all right for sealing parcels, but it is the last thing you should ever allow near your banknotes, because the

rubber solution eventually oozes out or loses its adhesive qualities and you end up with an ugly brown stain which can never be eradicated. It is far better to leave a torn note as it is than try to repair it with sticky tape.

It should be noted, however, that in the late eighteenth and early nineteenth centuries it was common practice for people sending banknotes through the post to cut them in half and send one half by one letter and the other half in a second letter, once the safe arrival of the first half had been intimated. Banks even provided special gummed strips, printed with the bank's name, to facilitate the re-union of the two pieces, and notes in this condition are eminently collectable as they demonstrate the mode of transmitting money by post before registration of letters was available.

Grading notes

With the development of the banknote market on a global scale, it is important that some commonly recognised system of grading notes is used as widely as possible. The following terms are now generally employed in auction catalogues and dealers' lists.

GEM CRISP UNCIRCULATED—the peak of perfection, describing a note as fresh as the moment it left the printing press.

CHOICE CRISP UNCIRCULATED—a note of only slightly lower standard, which may arise if it is not quite fully centred, or more likely will have very slight signs of handling.

CRISP UNCIRCULATED—at one time this meant what it said, but nowadays it is somewhat contradictory in that slight blemishes, such as a light bend in the centre or a minor corner crease (evidence of some degree of handling) would be permissible.

ALMOST/ABOUT UNCIRCULATED—nearly new, but with one light fold or slight evidence of corner creasing.

EXTREMELY FINE (EF)—a note showing

some signs of circulation but still in remarkably good condition and at least some of its pristine crispness.

VERY FINE (VF)—more evidence of circulation, with some creases or wrinkles but generally of a fine colour and appearance.

FINE (F)—a term which has now become so debased that it generally means the opposite. Such a note will bear the marks of circulation, with such blemishes as surface rubbing or fading. Such condition would not be acceptable for most notes of recent vintage, but would be allowed in the case of notes more than, say, 60–70 years old, or in the case of very rare notes.

VERY GOOD (VG)—actually quite worn, soiled and probably a bit ragged round the edges, but still acceptable on account of its age, so long as the design itself is not marred.

GOOD (G)—actually pretty poor, but acceptable only on account of the rarity or extreme historic interest of the note. Apart from dirt which may be removable or creasing which can be ironed out, such a note will be faded, rubbed or holed.

Mounting and housing notes

Certain museum collections and official bank archives are housed in cabinets with sliding frames in which banknotes are mounted on cards between glass panes. While this is a very attractive way of displaying a collection it is also very expensive and takes up a great deal of room. Until relatively recently most notaphilists were content to house their collections in conventional loose-leaf stamp albums, the notes being held in place by transparent mounting corners and the relevant data, such as date of issue, bank and country, could be written up on the page above each note. The disadvantage of this system is that only one side of the banknote could be examined without taking it out of its mounting corners.

An alternative to this, small transparent hinges, like those used by stamp collectors, were used to affix the notes to the album page. By this method the note could easily be turned over so that the back could be examined. This was considered more satisfactory, although many collectors felt uneasy about using stamp hinges which could leave an unsightly mark on the backs of notes and this would detract from their value. This method of mounting is certainly not recommended today.

The solution to these problems, widely disseminated in the 1970s, was the special album with plastic sleeves into which the notes could be inserted. These albums were actually produced initially for housing collections of postcards, but were found to be about the right size for banknotes. Unfortunately it was soon discovered that those sleeves made of polyvinyl chloride (PVC) reacted chemically with notes, either badly discolouring them or even depositing a viscous film on them. Subsequently better types of plastic such as Mylar film or polyethylene were developed, and these seem to have obviated the risk of contamination.

Today there are many different systems available to the note collector. There are cards (punched with holes to be inserted in ringbinders or peg-fitting albums) with clear rigid plastic fronts, as well as the more conventional "postcard" sleeves. The latter often come with black card inserts, so that notes can be inserted back to back, on either side of the card, but that then brings us back to the original album pages, with only one side of the note readily visible. There are also stout cards with a plastic face, slightly larger than postcard size, which can be stacked in a box or case, with the salient details of the note on narrow cards inserted at the top of the mount and then held upright as if in a filing cabinet. The main thing to remember is that, which ever system you adopt, you preserve your notes in a dust-free atmosphere, at an even temperature and humidity.

A popular banknote album from Lindner.

Around the world

Currency denominations of the world

Listed here are the names of all the currency units of the world found on paper money or coins. Many of them have been around for hundreds of years while others are no longer in use. Some of the denominations have been introduced only recently, whilst others are familiar household words. A number of the names are shared by different countries and a few have even been used by different civilisations.

Abbasi, Abbassi   Afghanistan, Georgia, Persia
Afghani   Afghanistan
Agora (ot)   Israel
Ahmadi   Mysore, Yemen
Amani   Afghanistan
Anna   Burma, India, Pakistan, Kenya, Muscat & Oman
Argentino   Argentina
Ariary   Malagasy Republic
Ashrafi   Afghanistan, Awadh, Bahawalpur, Egypt,   Hyderabad
At   Laos
Atia   Portuguese India
Att   Cambodia, Laos, Siam (Thailand)
Aurar (plural **Eyrir**)   Iceland
Austral   Argentina
Avo   Macau, Timor
Baht   Thailand
Baiocco (plural **Baiocchi**)   Papal States
Baisa   Oman
Baiza   Kuwait
Baizah   Muscat & Oman
Balboa   Panama
Ban (plural **Bani** or **Banu**)   Roumania
Banica   Croatia
Belga   Belgium
Besa (plural **Bese)**   Ethiopia, Somalia
Bipkwele   Equatorial Guinea
Bir (r)   Ethiopia
Bogach   Yemen
Bolivar   Venezuela
Boliviano   Bolivia
Butut   Gambia
Cache   French Indian Settlements
Candareen   China
Carbovanetz   Ukraine
Cash   China, Hong Kong, India, Mysore, Travancore, Turkestan, Vietnam
Cauri   Guinea
Cent   Australia, Bahamas, Barbados, Belize, Bermuda, Botswana, British East Caribbean Territories, British Honduras, British North Borneo, British Virgin Islands, Brunei, Canada, Cayman Island, Ceylon, China, Cochin China, Cocos (Keeling) Islands, Cook Islands, Curacao, Cyprus, Danish West Indies, East Africa, Ethiopia, Fiji, French Indochina, Gilbert and Ellice Islands, Guyana, Hawaii, Hong Kong, Indonesia, Jamaica, Kenya, Kiao Chau (Kiatschau), Kiribati, Laos, Liberia, Malaya, Malaysia, Malta, Mauritius, Netherlands, Netherlands Antilles, Netherlands Indies, New Zealand, Nova Scotia, Panama, Prince Edward Island, Sarawak, Seychelles, Sierra Leone, Singapore, Solomon Islands, South Africa, Sri Lanka, Straits Settlements, Suriname, Swaziland, Tanzania, Trinidad and Tobago, Tuvalu, Uganda, United States of America, Virgin Islands, Zanzibar, Zimbabwe
Centas (plural **Centa, Centu**)   Lithuania
Centavo   Angola, Argentina, Bolivia, Brazil, Cape Verde Islands, Chile, Colombia, Costa Rica, Cuba, Dominican Republic, Ecuador, El Salvador, Guatemala, Guinea-Bissau, Honduras, Mexico, Mozambique, Nicaragua, Paraguay, Peru, Philippines, Portugal, Portuguese Guinea, Portuguese India, Puerto Rico, St Thomas and Prince Islands, Timor, Venezuela
Centecimo   Bolivia
Centesimo   Bolivia, Chile, Dominican Republic, Ethiopia, Italian East Africa, Italy, Panama, Paraguay, San Marino, Somalia, Uruguay, Vatican
Centime   Algeria, Antwerp, Belgian Congo, Belgium, Cambodia, Cameroon, Cochin China, Comoro Islands, Djibouti, France, French Equatorial Africa, French Guiana, French Indochina, French Oceania, French Polynesia, French Somali Coast, French West Africa, Guadeloupe, Guinea, Haiti, Laos, Monaco, Morocco, New Caledonia, Reunion, Senegal, Switzerland, Togo, Tunisia, Vietnam, Westphalia, Yugoslavia, Zaire
Centimo   Costa Rica, Mozambique, Paraguay, Peru, Philippines, Puerto Rico, St Thomas and Prince Islands, Spain, Venezuela

Centu   Lithuania
Chervonetz (plural **Chervontzy**)   Russia
Chetrum   Bhutan
Cheun   South Korea
Chiao   China, Formosa, Manchukuo
Chi'en   China
Chio   China
Chon   Korea
Chuckram   Travancore
Colon   Costa Rica, El Salvador
Condor   Chile, Colombia, Ecuador
Cordoba   Nicaragua
Corona   Austrian provinces of Italy, Naples
Cruzadinho   Brazil, Portugal
Cruzado   Brazil, Portugal
Cruzeiro   Brazil
Deutschemark   Germany
Dinar   Afghanistan, Algeria, Bahrain, Hejaz, Iraq, Kuwait, Morocco, Persia, Saudi Arabia, Serbia, Tunisia, Turkey, Yugoslavia
Diner   Andorra
Dinero   Peru, Spain
Dirham   Jordan, Libya, Morocco, United Arab Emirates
Dirhem   Dubai, Iraq, Morocco, Qatar
Dollar   Anguilla, Antigua and Barbuda, Australia, Bahamas, Belize, Bermuda, Canada, Cayman Islands, China, Cocos (Keeling) Islands, Cook Islands, East Caribbean Territories, Fiji, Great Britain, Grenada, Guyana, Hawaii, Hong Kong, Indonesia, Jamaica, Japan, Kiribati, Liberia, Malaysia, Mauritius, Montserrat, Newfoundland, New Zealand, Panama, St Kitts-Nevis, St Lucia, St Vincent, Scotland, Sierra Leone, Singapore, Solomin Islands, Straits Settlements, Trinidad and Tobago, Tuvalu, USA, Virgin Islands, Western Samoa, Zimbabwe
Dong   Annam, Vietnam
Drachma   Crete, Greece
Dram   Armenia
Ekuele   Equatorial Guinea
Emalangeni   Swaziland
Escudo   Angola, Argentina, Azores, Bolivia, Cape Verde Islands, Central American Republic, Chile, Colombia, Costa Rica, Ecuador, Guadeloupe, Guatemala, Guinea-Bissau, Madeira, Mexico, Mozambique, Peru, Portugal, Portuguese Guinea/India, St Thomas and Prince Islands, Spain, Timor
Forint   Hungary
Franc   Algeria, Belgian Congo, Belgium, Burundi, Cambodia, Cameroon, Central African Republic, Chad, Comoro Islands, Congo, Danish West Indies, Djibouti, Dominican Republic, Ecuador, France, French Colonies, Gabon, Guadeloupe, Guinea, Ivory Coast, Katanga, Luxembourg, Madagascar, Malagasy Republic, Mali, Martinique, Mauretania, Monaco, Morocco, New Caledonia, New Hebrides, Reunion, Ruanda-Urundi, Rwanda, St Pierre and Miquelon, Senegal, Switzerland, Togo, Tunisia, West African States
Franchi   Switzerland
Frang   Luxembourg
Frank(en)   Belgium, Liechtenstein, Saar, Switzerland

Franka Ara   Albania
Gersh   Ethiopia
Girsh   Hejaz, Nejd, Saudi Arabia, Sudan
Golde   Sierra Leone
Grivna (plural **Grivny**)   Ukraine
Grosz (plural **Grosze** or **Groszy**)   Poland
Grush   Albania
Guarani   Paraguay
Guerche   Egypt, Saudi Arabia
Gulden   Austria, Curacao, German States, Netherlands, Netherlands Indies, Swiss Cantons
Habibi   Afghanistan
Hryvnia   Ukraine
Hsien   China
Hwan   Korea
Imadi   Yemen
Jeon   Korea
Jiao   People's Republic of China
Kapeikas   Latvia, Belarus
Kina   Papua New Guinea
Kip   Laos
Korona   Bohemia and Moravia, Hungary, Slovakia
Korun(a) (plural **Koruny** or **Koruncic**)   Czechoslo-vakia
Krajczar   Hungary
Kran   Iran, Persia
Kreu(t)zer   Austria, Austrian States, Czechoslovakia, German States, Hungary, Liechtenstein, Poland, Roumania, Swiss Cantons
Krona (plural **Kronor** or **Kronur**)   Iceland, Sweden
Krona (plural **Kroner** or **Kronen**)   Austria, Denmark, German States, Greenland, Liechtenstein, Norway
Kroon(i)   Estonia
Kuna (plural **Kune**)   Croatia
Kurus   Turkey
Kuta   Congo-Kinshasa, Zaire
Kwacha   Malawi, Zambia
Kwanza   Angola
Kyat   Burma, Myanmar
Lati, Lats   Latvia
Lei   Roumania
Lek (plural **Leke** or **Leku**)   Albania
Lempira   Honduras
Leone   Sierra Leone
Leu (plural **Lei**)   Roumania
Lev(a)   Bulgaria
Li   Manchukuo
Licente   Lesotho
Likuta   Zaire
Lilangeni   Swaziland
Lion d'Or   Austrian Netherlands
Lira (plural **Lire**)   Eritrea, Italian East Africa, Italy, San Marino, Syria, Turkey, Vatican
Lira (plural **Lirot**)   Israel
Lisente   Lesotho
Litas (plural **Litai** or **Litu**)   Lithuania
Luhlanga   Swaziland
Lweis   Angola
Macuta   Angola
Makuta   Zaire
Maloti   Lesotho
Mark   Germany, German States, German New Guinea, Norway, Poland, Sweden

Marka   Estonia
Markka   Finland
Metical   Mozambique
Milreis   Brazil
Mon   Japan, Ryukyu Islands
Mongo   Mongolia
Mun   Korea
Mung   Mongolia
Naira   Nigeria
Ngultrum   Bhutan
Ngwee   Zambia
Omani   Oman
Pa'anga   Tonga
Pahlavi   Iran
Pataca   Macau
Pengo   Hungary
Penni(a)   Finland
Perper(a)   Montenegro
Pesa   German East Africa
Peseta   Andorra, Equatorial Guinea, Peru, Spain
Pesewa   Ghana
Peso   Argentina, Bolivia, Cambodia, Chile, Colombia, Costa Rica, Cuba, Dominican Republic, El Salvador, Guatemala, Guinea-Bissau, Honduras, Mexico, Netherlands Antilles, Nicaragua, Paraguay, Peru, Philippines, Puerto Rico, Uruguay, Venezuela
Piastre   Annam, Cambodia, Cochin China, Cyprus, Denmark, Egypt, French Indochina, Hejaz, Iraq, Khmer, Lebanon, Libya, Nejd, Saudi Arabia, Syria, Sudan, Tonkin, Tunisia, Turkey, Vietnam, Yemen
Piso   Philippines
Pond   Transvaal
Pound   Ascension, Australia, Biafra, Cyprus, Egypt, Falkland Islands, Ghana, Gibraltar, Great Britain, Guernsey, Iran, Ireland, Isle of Man, Israel, Jersey, Malta, Nigeria, Rhodesia, St Helena, South Arabia, South Africa, Sudan, Syria
Pruta(ot)   Israel
Pul   Afghanistan, China, Turkestan
Pula   Botswana
Pya(t)   Burma
Qindar(ka)   Albania
Quetzal   Guatemala
Real(es)   Argentina, Bolivia, Central American Republic, Chile, Colombia, Costa Rica, Dominican Republic, Ecuador, El Salvador, Venezuela
Reichsmark   Germany
Reis   Angola, Azores, Brazil, Madeira, Mozambique, Portugal, Portuguese India
Rentenmark   Germany
Rial   Iran, Morocco, Muscat and Oman, Oman, Persia, Yemen Arab Republic
Riel   Kampuchea
Ringgit   Malaysia
Riyal   Iran, Iraq, Saudi Arabia, United Arab Emirates, Yemen Arab Republic
Rouble   Russia, USSR
Rubel   German occupation of Russia
Ruble   Poland, Transnistria
Rublis   Latvia
Rufiyaa   Maldive Islands
Rupee   Afghanistan, Andaman Islands, Bhutan, Burma, China, Cocos Keeling Islands, India, Iran, Kenya, Mauritius, Nepal, Pakistan, Saudi Arabia, Seychelles, Sri Lanka, Tanzania, Tibet, United Arab Emirates, Yemen
Rupia   Portuguese India, Somalia
Rupiah   Indonesia
Rupie   German East Africa
Ryal   England, Hejaz, Iran, Muscat and Oman, Nejd, Oman, Persia, Quaiti State, Saudi Arabia, Yemen, Zanzibar
Saidi   Oman
Satang   Siam (Thailand)
Scellino   Somalia
Schilling   Austria, German States, Poland, Swiss Cantons
Shahi   Afghanistan, Iran, Turkestan
Sheqal(im)   Israel
Shilingi   Tanzania
Shilling   Australia, Biafra, British West Africa, Canada, Cyprus, East Africa, Fiji, Gambia, Ghana, Great Britain, Grenada, Guernsey, Ireland, Isle of Man, Jamaica, Jersey, Kenya, Malawi, Malta, New Guinea, New Zealand, Nigeria, Scotland, Somalia, South Africa, Trinidad and Tobago, Uganda, Zambia
Sol(es)   Argentina, Haiti, Peru,
Soldo (plural **Soldi**)   Italian States, Swiss Cantons, Papal States,
Solot   Siam
Som   Kyrgyr Republic
Somalo   Somalia
Somoni   Tajikistan
Srang   Tibet
Sucre   Ecuador, Galapagos
Sueldo   Bolivia, Spain
Syli   Guinea
Tael   China, Laos
Taka   Bangladesh
Tala   Samoa, Tokelau
Talaro   Ethiopia
Taler   German States, Poland, Swiss Cantons
Tambala   Malawi
Tamlung   Siam
Tanga   Portuguese India
Tangka   Tibet
Tanka   Nepal
Thaler   Austria, Austrian States, Courland, Czechoslovakia, German States, Hungary, Liechtenstein, Poland, Roumania, Switzerland
Thebe   Botswana
Tical   Cambodia, Thailand
Toea   Papua New Guinea
Tola   India, Nepal
Tolar   Slovenia
Toman   Iran, Persia, Azerbaijan
Tughrik   Mongolia
Venezolano   Venezuela
Wan   Korea
Wark   Ethiopia
Warn   Korean
Wen   China
Whan   Korea
Won   South Korea
Xu   Vietnam
Yen   Japan
Yuan   China
Zaire Zaire
Zalat   Yemen Arab Republic
Zloty (plural **Zlote** or **Zlotych**)   Poland

29

Glossary of
banknote terms

Allied Military Currency Notes produced by the British and American governments for the use of military personnel in territories occupied during the World War II.

Alteration A deliberate change in some feature of a note, usually of a fraudulent nature.

Assignat Type of paper money used in France, 1789–96, representing confiscated Church land assigned to the holders.

Asterisk Note Note issued in Canada and New Zealand since ther 1950s to replace a defective note and so-called on account of the asterisk in the serial number.

Authorised Circulation The amount of money in notes which Scottish banks were permitted to have in circulation, under the Bank Act of 1845, based on a twelve-month average for the period prior to the Act coming into force. Any amount above this had to be backed by gold and silver.

Auxiliary Payment Certificate Form of paper money intended for use by American military personnel in overseas countries. See also Baf, Behelfszahlungsmittel and Scrip.

Babel Note Nickname derived from the biblical Tower of Babel, given to the paper currency of the Russian Socialist Federated Republic (1919) because it bore the slogan "workers of the world unite" in seven languages.

Back The side of a note generally regarded as of lesser importance than the front, and otherwise known as the reverse or verso. In early notes the back was often left blank, but in more recent times it has been used for a florid representation of the national arms or vignettes of scenery and landmarks.

Baf Acronym from British Armed Forces, the popular name for the vouchers which could only be exchanged for goods in service canteens from 1945 onwards.

Banknote Form of paper money issued by banks and usually promising to pay the bearer on demand in coin of the realm.

Banknote Strictly speaking, this is a piece of paper money issued by a bank, although the term is often loosely applied to any form of paper in circulation as currency.

Bearer Cheque A piece of paper which looks like a cheque but actually payable for the stated sum to any person holding it (the bearer) without requiring endorsement. Some of the emergency money used in Italy in the late 1970s consisted of such cheques.

Behelfszahlungsmittel German term for auxiliary payment certificates used in occupied Europe from 1939 to 1945.

Bill of Credit An American term denoting the paper money of the Colonial and early Continental period, from which comes the common expression 'bill' meaning a paper note.

Bill of Exchange The law defines this as "an unconditional order in writing, addressed by one person to another, signed by the person giving it, requiring the person to whom it is addressed to pay on demand or at a fixed or determinable future time, a sum certain in money to or to the order of a specified person or to bearers". It is addressed to a person or company, rather than a bank. The earliest examples are entirely handwritten although examples from the 19th century onwards often had the stock formula printed, with the details inserted by hand.

Billet de Confiance French for "tickets of trust", signifying small-denomination notes of the French Revolution issued to meet a shortage of coin due to hoarding.

Block Number Tiny numerals often found in the corners of notes, denoting the block or plate from which the notes were printed.

Bogus A note which is entirely false, in that it purports to be the money of a non-existent bank or country.

Bon Pour French for "good for", inscribed on tokens, coupons and vouchers which circulated as cash during periods of shortage of coinage.

Bond A certificate of intention to pay the holder a specified sum, with or without interest, on a specified date.

Bradbury Popular name for the UK Treasury notes introduced in August 1914 when specie payments were suspended on the outbreak of World War I, from the Treasury official, Sir John Bradbury, who signed them.

Braille   A system of reading by means of patterns of raised dots, invented by Louis Braille. In recent years such dots have been embossed on many banknotes to help identification by the blind and partially sighted, as well as provide an additional security feature.

Branch Banknote   A note which includes in its inscription a reference to the particular branch of a bank which issued it. In the USA such notes even had quite distinctive designs, but in England the name of the town or city sufficed to distinguish such notes from those of the head office in London.

British Armed Forces Special Voucher   Note issued from 1945 onwards for use in NAAFI canteens operated all over the world on behalf of the British armed services. Denominated in sterling, they could not be used outside the camp area and thus prevented black market operations between servicemen and the local population.

Broken Banknote   Note issued by a bank which has failed, but often applied more generally to banknotes which have been demonetised.

Burele   French term indicating a network of intersecting curved lines used as a security underprint.

Cancelled   A note withdrawn from circulation and rendered worthless by means of an overprint or perforated inscription, generally the word CANCELLED or its equivalent in other languages, e.g. Annule (French), Annulado (Spanish) or Ausser Kurs (German). Such notes sometimes come on to the market at a fraction of their original face value.

Carton   A form of soft card, much thicker than conventional paper, which has been used occasionally for emergency money, notably the small notes in Mexico, 1914–17.

Cartouche   Oval or circular frame enclosing a portrait or armorial device, setting it apart from the rest of the design.

Changeling   A note or cheque whose colour is altered from the norm as a result of exposure to humidity, sunlight or chemical action.

Chartered Bank   A bank operating under charter from the government, as opposed to a private or commercial bank.

Cheque   (American Check) A written order directing a bank to pay money.

Cheque Form   A printed form issued by banks for the convenience of customers. Collectors use this term to denote an unused cheque (preferably with the counterfoil still intact).

Chop   From the Hindi word chap, it means a stamp or seal used in India, China and other countries of Asia to make an official mark. The earliest paper money, for example, bore the chop of the Khan of Cathay, applied in vermilion, and this tradition continues to this day in the paper money of China and Japan.

Clearing Bank   A bank which is a member of a Clearing House.

Clearing House   A banking institution where notes and cheques are exchanged between banks.

Clearing House Certificate   A form of emergency money backed by coin or bullion deposited with the clearing house through which banks exchanged notes and cheques. Specifically the term is applied to American issues of 1907-8 and the early 1930s, during periods of economic crises and runs on banks.

Coin Note   A note issued by the US Treasury in 1890–1, so-called because it was redeemable in coin. A special reserve of silver dollars was established to cope with the redemption of these notes.

College Currency   Imitation money used in simulated transactions by business schools and colleges, mainly in the USA.

Colonial Currency   Paper money issued by the thirteen American colonies in the period from 1690 to 1776 or even later in some cases, before the emergence of the United States.

Colour Shifting Ink   Ink which appears to change colour as the note is tilted at a different angle.

Commemorative   A note issued for the specific purpose of marking a current event or the anniversary of a historic event or personality. Apart from notes with distinctive designs, such notes may consist of an additional or overprinted inscription, or even cyphers and serial numbers arranged in the form of anniversary dates or initials.

Company Note   A note issued by a commercial undertaking rather than a bank and redeemable in goods from the company store rather than actual cash. Such notes were common in Britain before they were rendered illegal by the Truck Acts of the 1840s.

Compound Interest Note   Note issued during the American Civil War, so-called on account of the six per cent interest which was compounded every six months.

Concentration Camp Money   Various forms of notes and vouchers produced immediately before and during the World War II in a number of Nazi concentration camps. These notes were intended to reward slave workers for their labour and were exchangeable for a limited range of goods, but more usually for such luxuries as the loan of library books or admission to camp concerts. Notes of this type are known to have been used in Oranienburg, Ravensbruck, Dachau, Sachsenhausen,

Buchenwald, Mauthausen, Auschwitz, Westerburg, Gross-Rosen and Mittelbau-Dora as well as in the ghettoes of Warsaw, Lodz (Litzmanstadt), Bielsk-Podlavsky and Theresienstadt. Notes denominated in US currency were also used in Deggendorf, Feldafing and Scheinfeld, former Nazi concentration camps which were used as displaced persons' camps, mainly for survivors of the Holocaust, prior to their immigration to Palestine in 1945–46. The British authorities also provided canteen money for Jews interned at camps in Cyprus in 1946–48, after being turned back from Palestine as illegal immigrants.

Continental Currency   Paper money authorised by the Continental Congress between 1775 and 1779 in the early stages of the American War of Independence.

Counterfeit   The forgery or imitation of a note intended for circulation to deceive the public and defraud the state or the issuing bank.

Counterfoil   The left-hand portion of a note or cheque, retained by the issuer as a record of the issue. It was usually divided from the main portion by some highly elaborate vertical design which, in the case of cheques especially, tended to become more pictorial in the 19th and early 20th centuries. From the 1840s the counterfoil was separated from the main part by some form of perforation, but earlier examples were cut apart by scissors, often in a serpentine or irregular line so that the two portions could be matched later on if required.

Coupon   Term from French *couper*, to cut, denoting a piece of paper which may be exchanged for goods or services, hence a detachable ticket or voucher entitling the holder to something. In the notaphilic context it denotes a detachable portion of a share certificate entitling the holder to a dividend, and has also been used to signify small notes used as emergency money.

Crossed Cheque   A cheque which bears parallel diagonal lines across the middle, either printed or handwritten, giving instructions to the paying bank to limit negotiability to the payee.

Crossing Stamp   A brass or rubber stamp applied by hand across the face of a cheque by the negotiating bank.

Currency   Notes intended to pass current in general circulation as money.

Current   Note still in circulation.

Cut Note   A note which has been officially cut into halves or quarters and re-issued, each part thereby serving as a note of appropriate value. As a rule, each portion bears an overprint signifying its new value.

Cypher   Term for the combination of letters which serve as a prefix in the serial number. In recent years such cyphers have often been deliberately contrived to serve a quasi-commemorative purpose, eg RLS (Robert Louis Stevenson), AGB (Alexander Graham Bell), SP (Scottish Parliament) and G/AD Glasgow, City of Architecture and Design) on Scottish notes of the 1990s.

Darlehnskassen   German for 'state loan note', a form of paper money issued during the World War I in an abortive bid to fill the shortage of coinage in circulation. These low-denomination notes failed to meet demand and were superseded by local issues of Notgeld in 1916.

Date   In many cases the year, or even a full date, merely denotes the point in time at which a note was authorised or introduced, and may antedate the actual time or even the year of release. In other cases, however, the date signifies the actual time of issue.

Demand Notes   Name generally given to the first series of paper money authorised by the US federal government by Act of Congress in 1861 at the beginning of the American Civil War, and so-called because the United States promised to pay the bearer on demand. The formula, of course, is widely used on the notes of many other countries and is by no means confined to the USA.

Demonetisation   The withdrawal of notes from circulation and declaring them to be worthless.

Denomination   The face value of a note, expressed in words of figures or often a combination of both.

Depression Scrip   American term for temporary makeshifts issued in various parts of the USA during the Depression of the early 1930s.

Device   Heraldic term for the pattern or emblem on banknotes.

Devil's Head   Collectors' term for certain notes of Canada and the Seychelles in which an image of the Devil was fancifully detected in the hair of Queen Elizabeth.

Die   Hardened piece of metal, usually steel but sometimes copper, bearing a positive image of the device to be transferred to the printing plate.

Die Proof   An impression, usually pulled on soft carton or India paper, of an intaglio engraving of a banknote, usually taken during the progress of engraving in order to check the detail. Proofs of this nature usually consist of the portrait or some detail of the design, such as the border, rather than the complete motif.

Dividend Warrant   A cheque issued in payment of a dividend to a shareholder, often attached to a document setting out the details of the dividend.

Dix Note   Collectors' term for $10 notes of the Citizens' Bank of Louisiana in New Orleans, from the French word DIX (ten) inscribed on their backs. The widespread notion that this gave rise to the term 'Dixie' denoting the Southern States of the USA is utterly false. Apart from the fact that many Canadian notes are similarly inscribed, it should be stated that the term 'Dixie', first popularised by the patriotic song of 1859 by Daniel D. Emmett, comes from the Mason-Dixon Line which separated the states of the free North and slave-owning South, Charles Mason and Jeremiah Dixon being the surveyors who mapped the southern boundary of Pennsylvania in the late 18th century.

Double Note   A note in which the front and back bear no relation to each other. This apparently first arose during the American Civil War when unfinished notes of a broken bank were pressed into service, with a new device on the blank side, by other banks as a result of a chronic shortage of paper.

Draft   An alternative name for a cheque, sometimes used in the context of a bank draft.

Drawer   The person drawing or issuing a cheque and whose signature appears on it.

Dual Currency   Notes inscribed with values in two different currency systems. This situation sometimes arises during a period of transition from one currency to another, usually as a result of monetary reforms.

Educational Notes   Name given to the US silver certificates of 1896 on account of the didactic nature of their designs.

Embossing   A printing process which entails the use of male and female dies or matrices to raise a portion of the design above the normal surface. It is commonly found on old cheques and bills of exchange which bear an embossed device denoting the payment of stamp duty, but in many banknotes of recent vintage it is used as a security device and an aid to blind and partially sighted persons to identify the face value correctly.

Emergency Money   Any form of money used in times of economic and political upheaval, when traditional kinds of currency are not available. In paper money this takes the form of all kinds of coupons, vouchers and scrip employed in military campaigns or in towns under siege, the Notgeld issued by many towns in Austria and Germany (1916–23), encased money, fractional currency, guerrilla notes, invasion, liberation and occupation money from the two world wars and minor campaigns. Among more recent examples may be cited the use of cheques in Italy (1976–77) and the issue of talons or coupons in many of the countries of the former Soviet Union pending the introduction of their own distinctive currencies.

Encased Money   Postage and revenue stamps enclosed in small metal and mica-faced discs, circulated as small change in times of emergency. The device was invented by John Gault, a Boston sewing-machine salesman, during the American Civil War (1862). The face of the stamp was visible through the transparent window, while the back of the disc was embossed with firms' advertisements. This practice was revived during and after the World War I when there was again a shortage of small coins. Encased stamps have also been recorded from Austria, France, Germany, Monaco and Norway. See also Stamp Money.

Endorsement   The signature of the payee on the back of a cheque.

Endorsement   Guarantee   A statement indemnifying the paying bank in the case of an incorrect endorsement on a cheque, usually indicated by means of a rubber handstamp.

Engine Turning   An intricate pattern of spiral and curved lines created by the Rose Engine, patented by Jacob Perkins between 1811 and 1819 as part of the process of steel engraving or siderography which established the fortunes of the security printing firm variously known as Perkins, Fairman & Heath, Perkins, Bacon & Heath or Perkins, Bacon. The French term guilloche is sometimes used.

Engraving   The art of cutting lines or grooves into a die for recess-printing (intaglio) or cutting away parts of the surface leaving the portion to be printed standing out (letterpress). See these terms for further details.

Error   Mistakes in paper money may be caused at the design or engraving stage, or as a result of a fault in the production processes. In the first category come misspellings in text or inscriptions, but more usually mistakes or inaccuracies in details of the design. In the second category the back of a note may be printed upside down in relation to the front, or a part of the design may be doubly printed or misplaced. Faulty registration of the printing plates may result in one colour being out of alignment. Other errors include serial numbers partially or wholly omitted or printed upside down. The commonest error consists of miscut notes.

Essay   (From the French essai, a trial piece).   In paper money this refers to any design, from the original artwork to a preliminary printing, for the purpose of examination by parliamentary or financial bodies, prior to the authorisation of an actual issue of notes, the counterpart of patterns in coinage or medals.

Face   The surface of a banknote, more usually referred to as the front, the recto or obverse.

Face Value   The value inscribed in words and/or figures at which the note passes current.

Facsimile   An imitation, usually authorised officially, of a note, perhaps created long after the original has been withdrawn from circulation. Such notes, usually marked in some way to indicate their true nature, were sometimes produced for exhibition purposes or to complete gaps in the bank's official collection, often utilising the original plates or dies.

Fantasy A note purporting to be the currency of a country which does not exist. Recent examples include the notes of the Hutt River Province which declared its independence of Western Australia.

Federal Reserve Bank Note Type of note issued by the Federal Reserve Bank of the USA between 1915 and 1933 and thus inscribed.

Federal Reserve Note A note issued by the Federal Reserve of the USA from 1914 to the present day and thus inscribed. These notes are backed by the federal government and not by individual banks.

Fei-ch'ien Chinese for "flying money", denoting the earliest form of paper money in the world and dating from the 7th–9th centuries.

Fiat Money Notes issued by a government but not redeemable in coin or bullion.

Fiduciary Issue Notes issued purely on trust, without the backing of gold or other securities.

Flying Money See Fei-ch'ien.

Forced Issue Paper money imposed on a populace without any backing and usually issued by the authority of an occupying power in time of war.

Forgery An unauthorised copy or imitation of a note, made with the intention of deceiving collectors. Forgeries intended to pass current for real notes are more properly termed counterfeits.

Foxing Unsightly spots, ranging from yellow to brown or dark red, caused by iron impurities in old paper. It is, in fact, a form of fungus which can spread across the paper or attack other paper with which it comes in contact. It can often be checked, if not always entirely eliminated, by treating the affected part with a very weak solution of a bleaching agent such as Chloramine-T. It is exacerbated by lack of air circulation and for that reason it is important that notes should be examined periodically and allowed to breathe.

Fractional Currency Emergency issue of small-denomination notes by the USA in 1863-65, following a shortage of coins caused by the Civil War. This issue was superseded by the Postage Currency notes, but bore the inscription "Receivable for all US stamps", alluding to the most popular medium of small change at that time. Denominations ranged from 3c to 50c.

Frame That part of the design forming the border, prevalent in note design until the 1960s when a much lighter, open style of design came into fashion. In many older notes the frame was elaborately engraved and ornamented to defeat counterfeiters.

Front The main side of a note, otherwise the obverse or recto, on which appears the name of the bank and/or country, together with signatures of bank officials, the date and place of issue and usually some form of promise to pay the bearer in coin of the realm.

Fund Raising Note A note produced by an exiled organisation to raise money for the campaign to gain independence. Good examples are the notes issued mainly in the USA by Irish and Hungarian nationalists in the 19th century.

Funeral Money Imitations of banknotes, used in China and Latin America in funeral ceremonies. See also Hell notes.

Gold Bank Note A note issued in the 1870s by nine banks in California and one in Boston, so-called because they promised to pay the bearer in gold coin.

Gold Certificate A series of nine issues in the USA between 1863 and 1922, redeemable in gold coin.

Gold Note Term generally applied to any note specifically redeemable in gold.

Goodfor Popular name for emergency money made of paper or card, from the inscription "Good for" or its equivalent in other languages (e.g. French bon pour or Dutch goed voor) followed by a monetary value. Notes of this type have been recorded from Europe, Africa and America during times of economic crises or shortage of coinage.

Granite Paper Type of security paper which has tiny coloured threads enmeshed in it.

Greenback Popular name for the paper money issued under the authority of the US government, from the predominant colour of the verso.

Guerrilla Money Money issued in areas under the control of guerrillas and partisans during wartime range from the veld ponds of the Boer War (1899–1902) to the notes issued by the Garibaldi Brigade in Italy and the anti-fascist notes of Tito's partisans in Yugoslavia. The most prolific issues were those produced in Luzon, Mindanao and Negros Occidental by the Filipino resistance (1942–45).

Guilloche French term signifying the intricate pattern of curved lines produced by the rose engine and used as a security feature in the production of banknotes, cheques, stocks and share certificates. See also engine turning.

Gutschein German word for voucher or coupon, denoting the paper money used aboard ships of the Imperial Navy during the World War I. The last issue was made at Scapa Flow, Orkney, during the internment of the High Seas Fleet (1918–19). The term is also widely used in Germany nowadays for any giveaway, exchangeable for goods or services as part of a sales promotion.

Halved Note   A note which has been cut in half as a precaution during transmission by post. On the safe arrival of the first half being notified, the other half is then sent by post. This practice was widespread in the early 19th century when highway robbery was prevalent. The two halves were subsequently re-united, often using specially printed strips of gummed paper.

Handsigned Notes which have been individually signed by hand, rather than by means of an engraved facsimile signature.

Hansatsu   Japanese term denoting notes of purely local validity, usually printed by woodblocks on soft, thick handmade paper, hence the derisive trerm "blotter money".

Hell Notes   Imitation paper money used in Chinese funeral ceremonies and buried with the dead to pay for services in the next world.

Holed   Term denoting notes which have either been pierced with pins or staples to attach them to each other or to documents, thereby detracting from their collectable condition, or notes which have been deliberately punched with small holes as a security precaution. The latter device is sometimes applied to specimen notes or printers' samples to prevent them getting into general circulation. See also perforated.

Hologram   A security device consisting of an image which changes colour or design depending on how it is tilted towards the light. It was first applied to credit cards in the early 1980s and to banknotes in 1988 (Australia), but has become much more widespread in very recent years.

Imitation Money   Also known as play money or toy money, it consists of notes produced for games of chance (like Monopoly), children's toy shops and post offices, as tourist souvenirs or for political satire (e.g. the shrinking pound or dollar). See also funeral money, hell notes and skit notes.

Imprint   Inscription on a note giving the name of the printer, usually found in the lower margin.

Indented   Description of an irregular edge on the left-hand side of a note, matching a corresponding pattern in the counterfoil, used in the 19th century as a precaution against forgery.

Inflation Money   Notes produced in Germany (1921–23), Austria (1923), Poland (1923), Hungary (1945–46), Greece (1946), China (1946–48) and many countries of Latin America and the former communist bloc since the 1980s and, most recently, by Angola and Turkey. Hungary holds the record for the highest value of any note ever issued—one thousand million adopengos equivalent to no less than 20,000,000,000,000,000,000,000,000,000 pengos.

Inscription   Any kind of text printed on the back or front of a note.

Intaglio   In the production of paper money, intaglio engraving is still commonly practised. In this process the engraver cuts the design into a steel die and the printing ink lies in the grooves. The paper is forced into the grooves under great pressure where it takes up the ink and results in the ridges which are characeristic of this process.

Interest Bearing Note   A note whose promise to pay the bearer includes a reference to interest payable at the time of redemption.

Invasion Money   Notes prepared in advance of a military invasion, either solely for the use of the invading forces, or also extended forcibly to the civil population and thus employed as means of controlling the local economy. *See also* liberation and occupation money.

Jugate   (From Latin Jugum, a yoke). Heraldic term denoting the overlapping profiles of two or more persons portrayed on banknotes. A good recent example is provided by the notes of Thailand celebrating the Golden Wedding of the King and Queen, released in April 2000.

Kreditivsedlar   (Swedish for "credit notes"). The name given to the first issue of paper money made in the western world. Paper money of this type was the invention of Johan Palmstruch at Riga in 1652 but nine years elapsed before it was implemented by the Stockholm Bank. The notes were issued up to 1666 and were mainly redeemable in copper platmynt though latterly in silver coin.

Labour Note   A form of paper money devised by the industrialist and philanthropist Robert Owen and used to pay his employees at the textile mills in New Lanark, Scotland in the 1830s. The value was expressed in hours worked rather than any monetary terms. The concept spread briefly to England and America, but was generally frowned on as an abuse of the workers' rights to spend their money freely, rather than at the company store.

Latent Image   A security device on a banknote which takes the form of an image that only becomes apparent when the surface of the note is tilted in a particular direction, and thus was a precursor of the hologram as a safeguard against forgery.

Leather Money   Pieces of leather embossed with an official device have been used as money on several occasions, during the sieges of Faenza and Leiden and in the Isle of Man in the 15th

35

and 16th centuries. Several towns in Austria and Germany produced lether tokens during and after the World War I.

Legal Tender Notes which are declared by law to be current money and which tradesmen and shopkeepers are obliged to accept in payment for goods or services. (*See* Banknotes and the Law).

Legend The inscription on a banknote.

Letterpress A printing process in which the ink is applied to the raised portions of a die or plate and then transferred to paper . It takes its name from the fact that this method was originally used in the printing of books and newspapers consisting mainly of lettering although from the outset it also included illustrations from woodblocks. This process is much cheaper and less secure than intaglio, and was used for many early banknotes. *See also* typeset.

Liberation Money Paper money prepared for use in parts of Europe and Asia, formerly under Axis occupation. Liberation notes were used in France, Belgium and the Netherlands in 1944-45, while various Japanese and Chinese notes were overprinted for use in Hong Kong when it was liberated in 1945. Indian notes overprinted for use in Burma were issued in 1945-46 when that country was freed from Japanese occupation.

Lithography A printing process patented by Alois Senefelder in 1795 and since widely used in the production of banknotes and cheques, mainly as an underprint, often in special fugitive inks. The name comes from the Greek lithos, a stone and graphein, to write, and alludes to the polished limestone slabs originally employed, although nowadays zinc or even paper plates are used instead. The image is laid down on the stone in greasy ink or by means of transfers. The printing ink adheres to the grease but is repelled by the blank areas of the plate.

Low Number A note with a very low serial number, either one or two digits preceded by a string of noughts, is regarded by collectors as very desirable, indicating very early issue. Pandering to this, however, many banks now set aside the low-numbered notes for inclusion in presentation folders sold to collectors.

Mandat Name given to a form of paper money issued in the period of the French Revolution. Like the assignat, which it replaced, the value of the mandat was theoretically backed by land confiscated from the Church and the aristocracy.

Margin That portion of a note lying between the outer border of the design and the edge of the paper. Notes with regular margins on all four sides often command a premium, whereas notes with irregular margins are often discounted. Margins may be clean-cut (by guillotine), rough or even deckle-edged if produced from individual pieces of handmade paper instead of being printed in sheets.

Master Die The original piece of steel or copper engraved by hand. It is then hardened chemically and an image taken by means of a transfer roller which, after hardening, transfers the image in reverse to the printing plate. Alterations to the master die, by means of punches or subsequent engraving, create secondary dies (often for the production of different denominations using the same basic design).

Metal Thread A security device in the form of a thin strip of metal embedded in the paper pulp during manufacture.

Microprint Printing in very tiny lettering, usually endlessly repeated, as a security precaution. It is often used in doubly fugitive ink on those parts of cheques where handwriting appears, to prevent attempts to alter or falsify details by washing, bleaching or chemical means.

Military Currency Notes issued under military authority, mainly for the use of troops on active service.

Military Payment Certificate A note produced by the US military authorities for the use of service personnel in PX (post exchange) canteens to prevent black market trading with local civilians.

Ming Note A large-sized Chinese note issued during the Ming Dynasty (1368-1644), using paper made from mulberry bark. Now highly desirable as the earliest form of paper money available to the collector market.

Miscut A note with very irregular margins, or even showing a portion of an adjoining note in the sheet, caused by misalignment of the blades cutting up the sheets of notes prior to issue. In some cases an additional piece of paper remains attached as a result of part of the wide sheet margin being accidentally folded over. Such errors in production are of curiosity interest rather than high monetary value, although they often command a premium.

Model A mock-up of a banknote, produced at a preliminary stage of production, often incorporated the pasted-up portions of previously issued notes or a composite of different elements which may eventually form the complete design,

Moiré French for "watering", denoting a security underprint of close wavy lines having the effect of watered silk.

Money Order Certificate for a specific amount of money, which may be transmitted by post and encashed at a money order office or post office. This system was pioneered by Britain and the USA in the early 19th century and is now virtually worldwide. The term is now confined to certificates above a certain value, the terms postal order and postal note being used for similar certificates covering small amounts.

Moses Crowns Popular name for the notes issued under the authority of the Jewish Council of Elders in Theresienstadt concentration camp during World War II, and so-called on account of the principal motif showing Moses holding up the Ten Commandments. *See also* concentration camp money.

Mule A note whose back and front are printed from plates which were not originally intended to be paired together.

Multilingual A note bearing inscriptions in many different languages. Apart from the so-called Babel notes of revolutionary Russia, good examples may be found in the issues of the Habsburg Empire, with values in up to eight languages and two scripts, or Indian notes with inscriptions in English and many different indigenous scripts. The Euro notes of the European Community bear the initials of the European Central Bank in the different languages and scripts of the member countries.

Multiple Denomination A note with values expressed in two or more different currencies, generally to facilitate exchange. *See also* dual currency.

National Bank Note American term applied specifically to the notes issued by banks, chartered by the federal government between 1863 and 1935, and backed by US Treasury bonds.

Negotiable Term applied to a banknote or cheque which can be readily converted into coin.

Notaphily Hybrid word from Latin nota (note) and Greek philos (love), coined in 1969 to denote the branch of numismatics devoted to the collection and study of paper money. *See also* syngraphics.

Note A piece of paper money. In former times the term was also loosely applied to cheques or IOUs.

Notgeld German word meaning "emergency money", applied to the various forms of currency, including notes, which circulated during the World War I when coinage disappeared from circulation, but rapidly overtaken by infinitely more prolific issues of paper money produced by shops, chambers of commerce, businesses and local authorities. Collectors distinguish between kleine Notgeld (small emergency money) in denominations from 10 to 50 pfennigs during and immediately after the war, and the large Notgeld whose denominations were in thousands, and later millions, of marks. Some 3,000 types appeared in 1922 and over 60,000 in 1923 alone. These quaint and colourful mementoes of the German hyperinflation ceased to circulate in 1924 when the currency was reformed.

Obsolete Term denoting a note which is no longer issued and has been withdrawn from circulation. Notes which are no longer issued but which may still be current during a brief overlapping period are more properly described as obsolescent.

Obverse The front of a note, equivalent to the "heads" side of a coin or medal, although the term recto is more appropriate for a piece of paper.

Occupation Money Any form of money, but usually notes or vouchers, issued in wartime by enemy forces in the territory which they invade and occupy.

Order Cheque A cheque payable to a specified person or to his or her order.

Out of Date Cheque A cheque which is considered by the paying bank to have been in circulation for "an unreasonable period of time". This is usually regarded as at least six months, although there is apparently no statutory limit.

Overprint Any form of printing added to a note or cheque after it was originally produced. Such a practice may be employed to alter the name of the issuing bank or authority or, in times of inflation and monetary reform, to convert the denomination to the reformed system. An overprint may also signify a change of government or regime, or even the name of the country.

Paid Cheque A cheque which has been honoured by a bank and the amount debited to the drawer's account.

Paid Stamp The handstamp applied to a cheque by the paying bank after debiting the sum to the drawer's account.

Paper Money Any form of currency based on paper.

Partisan Note A note produced by Tito's partisans operating in Serbia, Croatia and other parts of Yugoslavia after it was dismembered by the Axis during World War II, and used in those parts of the country which were effectively under their control.

Payee The person to whom a cheque is made payable.

Perforation A series of small holes punched out of paper. The earliest form, dating from the 1840s, was used to facilitate the separation of the cheque or banknote from its counterfoil, but later the punches were often arranged in the form of letters or numerals and could thus be applied to cheques to indicate the date on which they were presented for payment. In banknotes, perforation has sometimes been employed to mark them as Specimens intended for archival or publicity purposes and not valid for circulation. *See also* Cancelled.

Pilgrim Receipt A form of paper money overprinted for the use of people going on a religious pilgrimage. Notes of Pakistan, for example, are specially overprinted for use by pilgrims from that country making the haj to the Moslem holy places of Mecca and Medina in Saudi Arabia.

Pinhole A blemish on a banknote caused by it having been pinned or stapled to a document or another note. It should be noted, however, that certain notes only exist with this feature as they were put into circulation in batches stapled together for the sake of convenience.

Plain Back A note which has no printing of any kind on the reverse. *See also* Uniface.

Plate Number A small number incorporated in the design of some notes to indicate the plate from which it was printed.

Play Money Imitations of banknotes produced for use in such games of chance as Monopoly or as part of children's toy outfits for shops and post offices. Of passing interest to notaphilists only in so far as the designs are often vaguely derived from actual notes.

Playing Card Money A form of emergency money created in French Canada from 1685 onwards during shortages of coin supplied from France. Governor Duplessis hit upon using playing cards, with his signature and the denomination added in handwriting.

Polymer A chemical compound containing repeating structural units and formed by chemical combination of many small molecules. In notaphily the term is applied to various plastic materials used in the manufacture of banknotes since the 1970s.

Postage Currency Small notes in denominations of 5, 10, 25 and 50 cents, issued by the US federal government in 1862–63, were thus inscribed and had reproductions of postage stamps engraved on them—five 5c stamps on the 25c and five 10c stamps on the 50c notes. The earliest issue even had perforations in the manner of stamps, but this unnecessary device was soon dispensed with. *See also* stamp money.

Postal Notes or Orders Low-value notes intended for transmission by post and encashable at post offices. Introduced by Britain in 1883, they were an extension of the earlier money order system and are now issued by virtually every country.

Post-dated A cheque bearing a date subsequent to that on which it is presented for payment. As banks are not obliged to honour such cheques they are invariably handed back to the payee or returned to the drawer for re-presentation on or after the due date.

Prisoner of War Money Under the terns of the Geneva Convention the belligerents on both sides during the world wars provided special issues of notes for use within prisoner of war camps. Similar provisions were also made for the camps in which civilian enemy aliens were interned.

Promissory Note A written promise to pay, either on demand or at some future time, a sum of money to a specified individual or to the bearer.

Proof A preliminary test printing of the back or front of a note, taken from the master die or the printing plate before actual production, in order to ensure that every detail is correct.

Propaganda Note A piece of paper money containing political slogans or a didactic element. During the World War II forgeries of German and Japanese notes were produced by the Allies and additionally inscribed or overprinted with slogans such as "Co-Prosperity Sphere—What is it worth?" (a reference to the Japanese occupied areas of Southeast Asia). Forged dollars with Anti-American propaganda were airdropped over Sicily by the Germans in 1943 and counterfeit pounds with Arabic propaganda over Egypt in 1942-43. Various anti-communist organisations liberated propaganda forgeries of paper money by balloon over Eastern Europe during the Cold War period.

Provincial Note A note issued by a provincial bank or under the authority of a provincial government (as in Canada). Provincial banks in England were only permitted to issue notes so long as they did not have an office in London. The last of the English provincial banks was Fox, Fowler of Wellington Somerset, whose notes ceased in 1921 when the bank became part of the Lloyd's group.

Psywar Note A note produced as part of a campaign of psychological warfare. Effectively this means some kind of imitation paper money dropped as a leaflet by aircraft over enemy-held territory with the intention of demoralising the enemy and boosting the morale of the people enduring occupation.

Punched A note or cheque which bears the mark of a ticket punch to denote that it has been cancelled.

Rag Paper Paper made of linen rags, sometimes with an admixture of cotton or other textile substances, to produce a very tough, hard-wearing material for the production of banknotes.

Raised Note A note which has been revalued by means of an official overprint.

Reckoning Note A form of paper money issued to German troops on the eve of an invasion and exchangeable for local currency, usually at a considerable disadvantage to the economy of the occupied country.

Recto   The proper term for the face or front of a note.

Refunding Certificate   The official name for a $10 note issued by the US government in 1879 and made more acceptable to the general public on account of the 4 per cent interest per annum for an unspecified period. However, these notes were called in in 1907 by which time they were worth $21.30.

Reichskreditkassen   German for State Credit Treasury, inscribed on certain notes intended for circulation in occupied territories of Europe during the World War II.

Re-issue   A note issued again after an extended lapse of time.

Remainder   A note from a bank or issuing authority which has never been circulated, due to inflation, political changes or bank failure. Such notes, sometimes in partial or unfinished state (e.g. missing serial numbers or signatures) are generally unloaded on to the numismatic market at a nominal sum and provide a good source of inexpensive material for the beginner.

Repaired   A note which has suffered damage, usually tears or splitting, and bearing the evidence of having been restored. Unless they are very rare, such specimens are usually heavily discounted.

Replacement Note   A note issued to replace a defective note of the same serial number but generally identified as such by the inclusion of an asterisk of star alongside the number.

Reprint   A note produced from the original plates but long after production has been generally discontinued. Such notes often differ subtly from the originals, either in the type of paper used or, more often, in the shade of inks employed.

Revalidation   The process of bringing back into use notes which had previously been withdrawn from circulation and declared invalid. This has sometimes happened as a result of changes in political regime, such as in Austria where the notes of the early postwar period were similar to those immediately before the Nazi takeover in 1938, identifiable only by their dates.

Revalue   An overprint which alters the face value of a note, usually as a result of currency reform.

Reverse   The back of a note, more properly termed the verso.

Saddle Blanket   Nickname for the very large notes of the United States in the 19th century.

Safe Conduct Pass   A form of propaganda note airdropped behind enemy lines promising safe conduct to military personnel who decide to surrender.

Safety Paper   A form of security paper which dramatically changes colour (usually deep blue) when exposed to water. It was formerly widely used in the production of cheques, in order to deter people from trying to alter signatures or other handwritten portions by washing off the ink.

Scrip   Paper money of restricted validity or circulation, such as Bafs and other military notes used in service canteens and post exchanges.

Scripophily   Term coined in the 1970s to denote the study and collection of stocks, bond and share certificates.

Seal   A device, usually circular, which simulates the seal of a bank, a treasury or the state, formerly applied to documents in red sealing wax or embossed in metal foil, but now more generally applied by lithography or letterpress to the banknote design to enhance its official character. See also chop.

Sealskin Money   Notes of 1818-30 issued by the Russian Company trading in Alaska, using a form of parchment derived from the skins of seals.

Secret Mark   Any device concealed within the mass of engraving with the intention of tripping up the would-be counterfeiter. Such hidden marks, generally overlooked by forgers when fabricating notes, are known to the Secret Service (USA) and bank inspectors and are regarded as a test of genuineness.

Security Features   Since 1820 various devices have been incorporated in the design and production of banknotes in order to obviate forgery. These include guilloche engraving, watermarks, metal threads, granite paper, latent images, images visible only under ultra-violet light, microprinting, colour shifting ink, embossing, lithographic underprinting and holograms.

Segmented Security Thread   Security device in the form of a line of dashes running across the back of a note, either as a metallic thread or a minute holographic image.

Serial   The sequence of figures in numerical order which identifies each individual note. As a rule, numbers are combined with prefix and/or suffix letters which considerably extend the range of serials. As well as very low serial numbers, indicating early issue, collectors also take note of different styles or colours of figures and the presence of symbols (asterisks or stars) denoting replacement notes.

Series   A set of different denominations more or less issued within a clearly definable period if not always simultaneously, which possess common features in inscription, style or design. In some cases the word SERIES actually appears on the notes, followed by the date of its introduction.

Share Certificate   A piece of paper, often highly ornate or intricately printed, which certifies that the holder possesses a certain specified number of shares in a company.

Shinplasters   Derisory term originally applied to the Continental currency notes issued during the American War of Independence, the fractional currency of the Civil War period and also the low-denomination notes of Canada between 1870 and 1935, but often applied indiscriminately to any other low-denomination, small-format notes.

Shoshi   Adhesive stamps affixed to Japanese banknotes in the immediate postwar period in order to revalidate them.

Siderography   A printing process patented between 1811 and 1819 by Jacob Perkins and applied to the manufacture of printing plates for banknotes from 1820 onwards. From the Greek sideros, iron and graphein, to write.

Siege Note   A note produced by the defenders during the siege of a town, when supplies of normal currency are cut off. Notable examples include the notes issued at Venice during the Austrian siege of 1848 and by Mafeking in 1900 during the Boer War.

Sight Note   A type of promissory note, so-called on account of the formula "At . . . [number of days] after Sight, pay this to . . . Or Order, the Sum of . . ." Although in some cases the word "Sight" itself was inserted in manuscript, the period specified being usually 30 days.

Silk Thread   A security device patented in the 1830s by John Dickinson of Croxley Green and incorporated into some banknotes of the mid-19th century as a precursor of the metallic thread used nowadays.

Silver Certificate   Type of paper money introduced by the United States in 1878, redeemable by the Treasury in silver coin.

Signature   From the earliest times, bills, promissory notes, cheques and banknotes relied heavily on the signature of an individual or bank official. Handsigned notes survived in some instances until the late 19th century but from the 1820s onwards the vast majority of signatures have been engraved facsimiles. They are of importance to collectors as constituting a major variety in any series of notes, each change of signature constituting a collectable variant. One, two or three signatures of different bank officials are the norm, although notes of the Austro-Hungarian Bank had three Austrian and three Hungarian signatures, on front and back respectively.

Skit Note   A piece of paper masquerading as a banknote. It differs from a counterfeit in that its design parodies that of a genuine note, often for political, satirical or advertising reasons. Others were produced as April Fools' Day jokes or a form of Valentine (e.g. The Banks of Hearts or Lovers). In recent years they have been produced as advertising gimmicks or as coupons permitting a discount off the list price of goods. Also known as "Flash" notes.

Small Size Note   Collectors' term for the series of notes, in a reduced size from the preceding issues, which came into use in the USA in 1929 and are still in use.

Special Cheque   A cheque drawn on a form specially printed for the drawer and not of the standard design. Such cheques usually give far greater prominence to the names of the drawers (usually a company or institution) and may even be embellished with pictures of factories, premises or products. For this reason they are of immense interest to local historians.

Specie   Money in coin. Many issues of paper owe their existence to the suspension of specie payment in time of war or monetary crisis.

Specimen   Term generally used to denote a single item but more specifically applying to a note intended for circulation between banks or for press publicity and distinguished from the generally issued version by zero serial numbers, punch holes or a security overprint, usually the word SPECIMEN or its equivalent in other languages.

Stage Money   Notes specially printed for use in dramatic productions, on stage, screen or television, sometimes in vague imitation of real notes but often completely different to avoid any charge of counterfeiting.

Stamp Duty   A government tax on transactions involving money, and therefore applied in Britain to cheques between the beginning of the 19th century and 1962. The earliest duty was denoted by a colourless embossed stamp, followed in 1853-81 by various adhesive revenue stamps, then the small upright oval embossed stamps in red (1d) or blue (2d) and finally by the small circular crowned medallion stamps printed in black. Similar systems applied in many other countries. In the USA, for example, the duty could be denoted by a variety of adhesive stamps or by a device printed in orange-yellow across the middle of the cheque.

Stamped   Banknotes to which have been affixed adhesive stamps, either to denote the payment of a tax or to authenticate them. The latter practice has sometimes been used in lieu of an overprint to alter the validity of notes.

Stamp Money   Both postage and revenue stamps have circulated as money during shortages of coins, from the American Civil War onwards. Encased postage stamps were used in the USA (1861–62) before they were superseded by Postage Currency notes, but the same expedient was adopted by many other countries immediately after the World War I. Stamps afficed to special cards have circulated as money in Rhodesia (now Zimbabwe) in 1900, the French colonies and Turkey during the World War I, in Spain during the Civil War (1936–39) and the Philippines during the Japanese occupation (1942–45). Stamps printed on thick card, with an inscription on the reverse signifying their parity with silver coins, were issued in Russia (1917–18) and also in Armenia, the Crimea and the Ukraine (1918–20). During World War II Ceylon (which is now Sri Lanka) and several Indian states issued small money cards with contemporary stamps printed on them.

Star Note   A replacement note issued in the USA, so-called on account of the five-pointed star before or after the serial number.

State Bank Note   A note issued by a bank chartered by one of the states in the USA, as opposed to the issues of the Treasury, Federal Reserve or other agencies of the federal government.

State Note   A note issued in the early 19th century by one of the states in the USA.

Stopped Cheque   A cheque on which payment has been countermanded by the drawer before it is presented at the paying bank.

Stub   Another term for the counterfoil, retained as a record of a bank transaction.

Subject   Term indicating an individual note which is part of a sheet. Thus a 20-subject sheet would contain 20 impressions of the note.

Surface Printing   An alternative name for letterpress, the printing process mainly employed in the production of banknotes before 1820.

Sutlers' Notes   A form of scrip issued by US army canteen-keepers for use on military posts and redeemable in merchandise. They were mainly issued during the second half of the 19th century.

Syngraphics   Term coined in the 1970s, from the Greek syn (together) and graphein (to write) to denote the study and collection of cheques.

Travellers' Cheques   (American, Travelers' Checks) Notes in various denominations issued by Thomas Cook, American Express and many banks which can be converted into cash by tourists and businessmen when travelling abroad. They are validated by the traveller who signs each note in the presence of the issuing agent and then signs them again at the point of encashment. They are issued in sterling, US dollars or some other widely recognised currency but can then be converted into the equivalent in local money. Since the advent of credit cards and bank cards, however, the use of travellers' cheques has dropped very dramatically.

Treasury Note   Paper money worth 10 shillings or one pound, issued by the British treasury on the outbreak of the World War I when specie payments were suspended, and continuing till 1928 when the Bank of England took over responsibility for note-issuing. They were popularly known as Bradburys, from the signature of the Treasury official, Sir John Bradbury, engraved on them.

Type   A major design.

Typeset   A note in which the design is entirely composed of lettering, ornament being confined to printer's rule and the use of conventional symbols, usually to create a border.

Uncirculated   A note which is in the most perfect condition, as received at the bank from the printer and never passed from hand to hand.

Uncut   A sheet or part of a sheet in which two or more notes are still unsevered.

Underprint   The background to the principal motif and inscriptions of a banknote, generally printed by a different process (e.g. lithography instead of intaglio) and in contrasting, lighter colours incorporating security features such as microprinting and latent images.

Uniface   A note which has printing on one side only.

Upham   A Philadelphia printer whose patriotism during the Civil War led him to produce facsimiles of Confederate notes. The reproduction was excellent and the imitations could only be readily distinguished by Upham's imprint and advertisement in the bottom margin. Unfortunately most of his notes had the advert trimmed off and swiftly found their way to the Confederacy where they were promptly circulated as genuine. As a result, Upham facsimiles with the imprint still intact are now relatively scarce, and certainly rarer than the notes they imitated.

Validating Stamp   A handstruck mark applied to notes either at the time of issue to render them valid or subsequently applied to extend their usage.

Varible Optical Ink   Ink which appears to change colour or density depending on the angle at which the note is viewed.

Variety   Variation in, or modification of type, effigy or inscription.

Verso   The proper term for the reverse or back of a note.

Victory Note   A banknote of the Philippines overprinted VICTORY from October 20, 1944 onwards to celebrate the liberation of the islands after almost three years of Japanese rule.

Vignette   Strictly speaking the pictorial element of a note, shading off into the surrounding unprinted paper rather than having a clearly defined border or frame, but nowadays applied generally to the picture portion of a banknote, as opposed to the portrait, armorial or numeral elements.

Voucher   A piece of paper exchangeable for goods or services of a specified value and therefore regarded as a form of paper money.

War Lord Note   A note issued by one of the many tuchuns or war lords who operated in various parts of China in the period between the fall of the Manchu Dynasty and the communist takeover in 1949. Seldom, if ever, backed by gold or collateral other than the barrel of the gun, these notes were often well designed and printed (employing the leading security printers of Europe and America to lend them respectability), but rendered worthless as the fortunes of civil war ebbed and flowed. They have left a rich legacy of relatively cheap but colourful material for the collector market.

Watermark   A security device, generally visible when the note is held up to the light, and ranging from an overall geometric or curvilinear pattern to state emblems and even portraits, the lastnamed often set within a circular or oval cartouche. The watermark derives its name from the fact that it is created at the wet pulp stage in the manufacture of the paper, in which the pressure from brass wires or "bits" of the required pattern causes a slight thinning in the paper. In some cases notes have been printed on paper bearing the papermaker's name or trademark, only a portion of which is visible on any one note.

White Note   Collector's term for the early notes of the Bank of England which were printed in black ink on white paper, using a relatively large format. This tradition, dating from 1695, continued as late as 1957 when the "white fiver" was superseded by a £5 note of more conventional design. These white notes were deceptively simple, which may have encouraged the Germans, under Operation Bernhard, to forge them during the World War II, using skilled counterfeiters in prisons and concentration camps for the purpose. But in fact the secret of these notes lay in the quality of paper used, with its extremely intricate watermark pattern, and it was the failure to secure paper of the right quality which defeated the forgers in the long run.

Wildcat Notes   Notes issued in the USA and Canada in the early 19th century by unscrupulous persons who purported to act on behalf of non-existent banks. Poor communications and lax banking laws enabled them to get away with these frauds for a short time before their notes were unmasked as false and worthless. Nevertheless they are not without considerable interest on account of their colourful designs and their role in the rather freewheeling commerce of the period.

Withdrawn Note   A note which has been taken out of circulation. Sometimes, though by no means always, such notes are overprinted, perforated or punched in some way to indicate that they have no legal tender status or any actual worth.

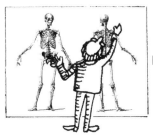

The anatomy
of a banknote

Below we illustrate some typical banknotes in order to show the various elements which combine to make up the design. Modern banknotes generally involve two or more different printing processes, applied to specially prepared paper which may incorporate one or more security features. The notes reproduced here have been chosen to represent the various details which the collector is likely to encounter in notes in general, as well as demonstrate how the design is built up as a result of very considerable thought—even though most members of the public may never give it a second glance.

Bank of England £20

Front (Obverse)

1. Denomination, comprising the pound sign £ (from Latin Libra = pound) and numerals, both horizontally lined and in contrasting colours.
2. Numerals of value (upper right) cross-hatched.
3. Bank of England in Old English upper and lower case lettering.
4. Paraphs or flourishes for decorative effect.
5. Promise: I PROMISE TO PAY THE BEARER ON DEMAND THE SUM OF TWENTY Pounds in three different fonts.
6. Signature of Merlyn Lowther who personally makes the promise in her capacity as Chief Cashier.
7. Cypher or serial, consisting of a two-letter prefix followed by eight digits. The left-hand cypher is made up of numerals of varying sizes and colours, whereas that on the right is of uniform size and colour.
8. Three-quarter facing portrait of Her Majesty Queen Elizabeth.
9. Hologram, crowned and scrolled, containing the seated figure of Britannia, based on the original motif, with the numerals 20 in an overall background pattern. Tilt the note in another direction and the image appears as 20

on an engine-turned background. In both positions, microscopic numerals also appear across the foot.
10. Place of issue: "London, For the Govr. and Compa. of the BANK of ENGLAND" in antique copperplate script.
11. Watermark, showing a bareheaded portrait of Queen Elizabeth.
12. The Royal monogram E II R on a solid rectangular ground.
13. Copyright symbol followed by THE GOVERNOR AND COMPANY OF THE BANK OF ENGLAND, 1999.
14. Musical notes, symbolising the subject on the back of the note.
15. Continuous band inscribed £20 in microprint.
16. Value in words TWENTY POUNDS in microprint on a lithographed underprint.
17. Underprint consisting of a subtly changing pattern of ornament and wavy lines.
18. Anaglyphic pattern, creating the illusion of a three-dimensional motif.
19. Band containing word TWENTY and numerals 20 alternately.
Plus a solid vertical metal strip showing through when viewed from the front.

Back (Reverse)

1. Vertical metal strip showing as short dashes.
2. BANK OF ENGLAND in double-lined capitals.
3. Value £20 in different styles in the upper corners.
4. Portrait of the composer, Sir Edward Elgar (1857-1934).
5. View of the West Face of Worcester Catherdal.
6. St Cecilia, patron saint of music.
7. Angel blowing a trumpet.
8. Latin motto.
9. Underprint of musical notes and symbols, repeated in various colours.
10. Copyright symbol and text around the watermark portrait.

The bulk of the detail on the reverse is lithographed, but the inscriptions are intaglio, like most of the features on the front.

United States $1

Front (Obverse)

1. Border title: FEDERAL RESERVE NOTE
2. Country name: UNITED STATES OF AMERICA
3. Legal Tender statement.
4. Numerals of value: two different sizes and different frames
5. Green serial, upper right and lower left, consisting of a district letter (L), 8-digit number from 00000001 to 99999999, and a suffix letter. The serial is repeated in opposite corners in case of accidental damage to part of the note.
6. Check letter and quadrant number (upper left), denoting the position of the note on the printing plate.
7. Check letter and plate number (lower right), denoting the actual plate used for printing.
8. District number 8, appearing in four positions, and indicating Federal Reserve District of St Louis.
9. District letter H contained in the seal of the Federal Reserve Bank. The district numbers and letters are: A1 (Boston), 2B (New York), 3C (Philadelphia), 4D (Cleveland), 5E (Richmond), 6F (Atlanta), 7G (Chicago), 8H (St Louis), 9I (Minneapolis), 10J (Kansas City), 11K (Dallas) and 12L (San Francisco).
10. Treasury seal, in green.
11. Value expressed as the word ONE in double-lined shaded lettering.
12. Upright cartouche, framing a bust portrait of George Washington, first President (1789-97), after the painting by Gilbert Stuart.
13. Background of cross-hatching.
14. Signature of Mary Ellen Withrow, Treasurer of the United States.
15. Signature of Robert E. Rubin, Secretary of the Treasury.
16. Series 1995. The year indicates when the design was introduced in its present form, if a letter is also present this denotes modification to the design.
17. Border of guilloche or engine-turning, to defeat counterfeiting.
18. Value in words ONE DOLLAR in bottom border.

Back ((Reverse)

1. Country name in white on green engine-turned background.
2. Value as a word superimposed on a numeral, in all four corners.
3. Motto IN GOD WE TRUST, added in 1957.
4. Value in word ONE in ornamental shaded lettering.
5. Plate number.
6. Value in words ONE DOLLAR, in shaded capitals, across the foot.
7. Reverse of the Great Seal of the United States:
8. Latin motto ANNUIT COEPTIS (He has favoured our undertakings) made up of 13 letters representing the original states.
9. The eternal eye of God, symbolising the spiritual over the material.
10. Pyramid of 13 tiers representing solid foundations and strength, but top unfinished to symbolise perfection as the ultimate goal.
11. Roman numerals for 1876, centennial year of the United States.
12. Latin motto NOVUS ORDO SECLORUM (a new order of the ages).
13. Obverse of the Great Seal of the United States:
14. Glory, comprising 13 five-pointed stars in a sunburst.
15. Riband motto in Latin E PLURIBUS UNUM (out of many, one).
16. Eagle's head representing the Executive Branch of government.
17. Shield with 13 stripes symbolising Congress and national unity.
18. Talons holding an olive branch of 13 leaves, symbolising a desire for peace.
19. Talons holding 13 arrows. symbolising readiness for war.
20. Nine tail feathers, symbolising the Supreme Court and Judiciary.
21. Scrollwork ornament.
22. Reticulation.
23. Beading.

There is also an albino colourless impression round the outer edges of the design, from the engraving on the front. Most of the black (front) and green (back) printing is intaglio, but the Treasury seal is lithographed and the district numbers and serial are letterpress. The paper has a security watermark overall, as well as small coloured threads embedded in the surface.

A brief history
of paper money

The late Enoch Powell, a politician who was also a well-known numismatist, once scathingly dismissed paper money as something "which does duty for money in our degenerate age". From this it would be reasonable to suppose that paper money is a tawdry substitute for the real thing—gold and silver—in an age when money has ceased to have real value. With mounting inflation and continual rises in prices, many people would be inclined to agree; but while it is true that paper money has been used to a very large extent in the past century, it is by no means a modern phenomenon. In Britain, America and many European countries, paper money was in use three centuries ago. In Asia, however, paper was being used as money while Europe was still in the Dark Ages.

Appropriately enough, paper money began in China where paper itself was invented. The earliest form of paper money was produced during the T'ang Dynasty, somewhere between 650 and 800 AD. At that time the coins used in China were made of bronze, and very large quantities of bronze *cash* were needed for even the smallest transactions. This was not only inconvenient because of its weight, but also rather insecure. The cumbersome wagons used to carry these coins from one part of the country to the other were likely to ambushed by bandits and it was in an attempt to foil highway robbers that the Chinese merchants invented *fei-ch'ien*, literally "flying money", consisting of paper drafts negotiable in bronze currency. These drafts were not authorised paper money in the modern sense, but they undoubtedly paved the way for the

An early Chinese printer.

paper money introduced by the Sung Dynasty about 1000 AD. These Sung notes were redeemable in coin and quickly gained acceptance.

Unfortunately, the number of banks grew rapidly (there were no fewer than sixteen in Szechuan province alone) and they were all too readily tempted into issuing more and more notes without the funds or assets to back them. These notes, known as *chiao-tzu* (exchangeable money) soon lost the confidence of the people whereupon the government began issuing *kuan-tzu* (citadel money) which, in turn, was over-issued and led to an inflation which contributed to the downfall of the Sung Dynasty in 1278.

Their successors, the Yuan Dynasty (1270–1368) also issued far too much paper money. Before the end of the Mongol occupation of China this paper money had been reduced to utter worthlessness. A few examples of these very large and impressive notes have survived to this day, but rather more plentiful are the notes produced by the Ming Dynasty (1368–1644). They were made from the bark of the mulberry tree and printed from wooden blocks. Marco Polo describes in some detail the paper money of Cathay, as China was then known:

"All these pieces of paper money are issued with as much solemnity and authority as if they were of pure gold or silver; and on every piece a variety of officials, whose duty it is, have to write their names, and to put their seals. And when all is prepared duly, the chief officer deputed by the Khan smears the seal entrusted to him with vermilion, and impresses it on the paper, so that the form of the seal remains printed upon it in red; the money is then authentic. And the Khan causes every year to be made such a vast quantity of this money which costs him nothing, that it must equal in amount all the treasure in the world. When any of those pieces of paper

are spoilt—not that they are so very flimsy either—the owner carries them to the mint, and by paying three per cent on the value he gets new pieces in exchange."

With the collapse of the Ming Dynasty in 1644 the use of paper money came to an end. Two centuries later, however, the economic crisis caused by the T'ai-ping Rebellion of 1853–64 led the imperial government to resurrect paper money as an easy way out of its financial difficulties. From then onwards China became one of the world's most enthusiastic issuers of paper currency, with disastrous results on the economy and political stability of the country, especially in the turbulent period between the world wars when large parts of the country were under the control of various warlords.

The designs of the early Chinese notes were often very elaborate, and usually had some religious significance. The *chops*, or seal marks, added in vermilion ink to make these notes authentic, were inscribed in Chinese characters and took the form of such phrases as "to circulate as cash" or "to circulate under the Heavens". Some notes even depicted a number of coins, of the equivalent value, so that no one would be in any doubt as to the value of the note.

Banking in Europe

There are numerous references in the Bible and the literature of ancient times to moneylenders and others who, in effect, were the world's first bankers. The Babylonians, Egyptians, Greeks and Romans all had elaborate banking systems whereby rich merchants and goldsmiths lent money to businessmen or stored money for others. In Mesopotamia, the Igibi Bank is known to have been lending money and taking deposits in the middle of the sixth century BC, if not earlier.

Banking transactions are referred to frequently in accounts of life in Roman times. In medieval Europe, the rich merchants of the Italian cities of Milan, Venice and Genoa, the Hanseatic ports of Hamburg and Lubeck, and the international towns of Antwerp, Bruges and Geneva were acting as bankers, lending and receiving vast sums of money.

Many of these transactions were done on paper

Rich merchants and traders of Antwerp.

or parchment and took the form of promissory notes. Merchant "A" would give a note to a banker "B" promising to pay him 100 marks when his ship returned with a cargo from the East. The banker "B" might then use the note to pay goldsmith "C" for a quantity of silver or gold. Goldsmith "C" might use the note to pay farmer "D" for a quantity of corn. Finally the farmer would present the note to the original merchant "A" when the date for payment fell due, and demand 100 marks in coin. In this way promissory notes came to be accepted in much the same way that we use paper money today. Sometimes these notes might pass from hand to hand for a considerable time before they were eventually presented to the original issuer for redemption.

The earliest promissory notes would have been made of vellum, parchment or some other kind of animal skin. Paper was virtually unknown outside China until the middle of the twelfth century and came to Europe via Arabia and North Africa. Herault in France claims to have had the first paper mill in Europe, established in 1189. For hundreds of years thereafter paper continued to be a scarce commodity in Europe. In England the earliest kind of paper money consisted of notes issued by goldsmiths as receipts for valuables deposited by merchants in their vaults. These receipts could be used as securities to get a loan and, like promissory notes, tended to circulate quite widely as a form of currency. These receipts and promissory notes were accepted as legal tender following an Exchequer Order made by the authority of King Charles II in 1665, but another thirty years elapsed before paper money, as we understand it today, was issued in Britain.

The first paper money to be issued in Europe made its appearance in 1661. The Stockholm Bank of Sweden issued credit notes (*kreditivsedlar*) in place of the very cumbersome copper currency which was rapidly losing its value. The idea of producing these notes originated with Johan Palmstruch, a Dutchman living in the Latvian city of Riga (which was then a part of Sweden). Palmstruch put forward this idea in 1652. His notes

The introduction of weights and measures into Greece occurred alongside the introduction of coined money.

were the first banknotes in the modern sense and not like the previous receipts given by goldsmiths and merchant bankers for specific deposits. They were current in the hand of the bearer and did not earn interest, as the promissory notes often did.

None of the first issue of *kreditivsedlar* has survived and fewer than a dozen specimens of the issue of 1662 and 1663 are now in existence, all in various museum collections. The issue of 1666, however, is much more plentiful, though this was the last to appear. These notes seem to have been readily accepted by Swedish businessmen, being much more convenient to handle than the cumbersome copper plate-money, but the Stockholm Bank gave way to the temptation of over-issuing. As early as 1663, the Bank was unable to redeem its notes and two years later the Swedish government decided that they should be abolished. The last issue was redeemable in silver thalers, since copper went out of circulation in 1665–6.

The founding of the Bank of England, 1694.

Paper money became popular at the end of the seventeenth century in Britain and France, thanks largely to the efforts of two Scotsmen. William Paterson founded the Bank of England in 1694 and the Bank of Scotland the following year. His fellow countryman, John Law, founded the first French bank, the *Banque Generale,* in 1716. Both men realised the convenience and advantages of paper money and were responsible for the first issues of banknotes on both sides of the English Channel.

The earliest notes of the Bank of England were issued in 1695 and were in denominations of £10, £20, £30, £40, £50 and £100. Altogether some 12,000 notes were issued in 1695–6. The notes were large in size and beautifully printed in black copperplate

on white paper made of a mixture of linen rags and cotton. The date, bearer's name and cashier's signature were entered in handwriting, while the rest was printed.

In the top centre was a little picture of Britannia seated and holding a spear and an olive branch. At her side was a shield bearing the cross of St George and at her feet was a pile of coins. At first the value of the note was printed, but later issues showed the amount in handwriting. The same basic design was retained for the higher-value Bank of England notes until 1956. Many people will recall the old-style "white fivers". Partly because of their high value and partly on account of fear of forgery, tradesmen and shopkeepers used to insist on their customers writing their names and addresses on these notes whenever they offered them in transactions, while examples passing through post offices often bore the office postmark as well.

After founding the *Banque Generale* John Law formed the French Mississippi Company of Louisiana in 1718 and speculation in its shares was equalled only by the British South Seas Company. Like the latter, the bubble burst in 1720 and Law (who by this time had been appointed Comptroller General of France) had to flee the country. Under John Law, the *Banque Generale* also issued its own notes, but these were quite ordinary in appearance. Apart from their serial number, which was written in by hand, the notes were printed in black on white paper and promised the bearer on demand various sums in livres Tournois coined in silver.

Examples of these notes, issued at Paris between 1716 and 1720, are now quite scarce. Law had several theories regarding economics and though he was discredited in 1720 his ideas survived him, to cause untold misery and financial chaos to his adopted country. He had proposed a land currency equal to the value of the land and to the value of actual coined money without being subject, as was coined money, to a fall in value. This system was adopted by the French government, when on the verge of bankruptcy, and this precipitated the Revolution of 1789–92.

Notes known as *Assignats* were issued issued in 1789, their value backed by the land confiscated from the Church at the outset of the Revolution. Each note had a nominal value of 100 livres bearing interest at 5 per cent. A total of 4,000 million livres was put into circulation in the first issue alone. Within a year the interest had been reduced to 3 per cent and a subsequent issue of 800 million livres bore no interest at all. The output of paper money grew faster and faster; by the middle of 1794, a total of 8,000 millions had been issued, but within two years the amount in circulation had spiralled to 45,500 millions. The value of the *assignat* fell rapidly. Even the earlier issues were reckoned to be worth only 20 livres in coin for every 100 livres in paper. By 1793 the depreciation had reached 97 per cent. The government body known as the

Directory fixed the value of the *assignats* at a thirtieth of their original value and then reduced it to a hundredth.

When the *assignats* sank to utter worthlessness the government had recourse to territorial money orders known as *Mandats* which were put into circulation at the rate of one for 30 *assignats*. These notes were no more trusted than the *assignats* and actually depreciated more rapidly. In many cases the *mandats* were worthless before they could even get into circulation. The Directory finally gave up its experiments with paper money in 1797 when *assignats* and *mandats* were called in and exchanged for coin in the ratio of one livre for every 3,000 livres paper money.

British Banks

Meanwhile, in England, the banking system developed along much sounder lines. By the 1680s there were about fifty merchants in London alone whose promissory notes were readily acceptable and these entrepreneurs were the founders of banks that bore their names, such as Martin's, Barclay's, Lloyd's, Glyn Mills, Coutts and Cox & King's. Regular denominations, from £20 to £1,000, were resumed by the Bank of England in 1725, notes for £10 and £15 being added in 1759. As the Bank of England did not issue notes of lower value it was left to the many private banks, which mushroomed in the eighteenth century, to remedy this deficiency. Some attempt to regulate this industry came by way of an Act of 1777 which forbade the private banks to issue notes under £5. Nevertheless small provincial banks came and went with alarming rapidity and in 1793 alone more than a hundred of them crashed. In that year the Bank of England issued its first £5 notes and

A Bank of England £1 note of 1797.

four years later the 1777 Act was repealed in order that the Bank could issue £1 and £2 notes.

During the French Revolutionary and Napoleonic Wars, gold and silver coins were in short supply, and the private banks filled the gap with numerous issues of notes. By 1810 there were more than 700 banks in operation in England and Wales alone, issuing more than £30 million each year. The wartime boom was followed by a slump in which many of the smaller banks disappeared

or were taken over by their larger competitors. In November 1825 many companies went bankrupt and this precipitated a run on the banks. The position was exacerbated when many provincial banks could not get at the funds which they, in turn, had deposited with the major London banks. When one of the major London banks failed early in December 1825 no fewer than 44 provincial banks crashed as a result. By December 17 four of the biggest London banks had ceased payment and the Bank of England's gold reserve was down to less than a million pounds.

To alleviate the situation the Bank hastily issued a large quantity of £1 notes which had been partially prepared for release in 1821 but had never been put into circulation. These notes bore the date 1821 at the top, but were dated 20 December 1825 at the foot. They circulated for a few months, until the Bank of England was able to replenish its stocks of gold with the assistance of Rothschilds, the French merchant bankers. From then until 1928 the Bank of England did not issue notes below £5 in face value.

In the economic crisis of 1825–26 hundreds of country banks went out of business and are remembered nowadays solely on account of their notes, many of which were attractively engraved with local landmarks and scenery. The notes of the broken banks are also of interest for the marks stamped on them indicating that they were produced in evidence in the bankruptcy courts. Many of them also have marks indicating how much was actually paid out to creditors in the end.

The Bank Charter Act of 1844 limited the number of note-issuing banks to 72 joint stock banks and 207 others, with a total note issue of £8,500,000. Thereafter the number of note-issuing banks dwindled. Under the terms of the 1844 Act no bank with offices in London could issue its own notes. As more and more of the provincial banks were taken over by London-based banks their privilege of issuing notes was curtailed. The last of the independent note-issuing banks was Fox, Fowler & Company of Wellington, Somerset which gave up this privilege in 1921 when it amalgamated with Lloyd's Bank.

Private banknotes continued to appear in the Isle of Man until 1961 when the Manx government took over the privilege hitherto enjoyed by the Isle of Man Bank, Lloyd's, Martin's and Barclay's. Since then, notes have been issued by the Isle of Man Bank under the authority of the Isle of Man government.

Scotland and Ireland have been issuing their own banknotes since 1696 and 1783 respectively and since the Bank Charter Act of 1844 did not apply to these countries, the private banks retained the right to issue their own notes. At the end of the World War II there were still about a dozen Scottish banks issuing distinctive notes in denominations from £1 upwards, but as a result of mergers and take-overs the number has now fallen to three. In

Guernsey notes issued during the German occupation in World War II.

Northern Ireland a number of banks continue to issue their own notes but in the Republic of Ireland notes are now confined to the issues of the Bank of Ireland. In the Channel Islands notes were issued by various private banks from 1797 onwards, while the States of Guernsey produced the first government notes in 1826. Of particular interest are the notes, ranging from sixpence to £5, issued by Guernsey and Jersey during the German occupation (1940–45). Attractive banknotes are produced to this day by the state banks in both bailiwicks.

In Britain, the gold sovereign and half-sovereign continued to be the preferred medium in circulation, but on the outbreak of the World War I in August 1914 specie payments were suspended and the government authorised the Treasury to issue notes of £1 and 10s, popularly known as Bradburies because they bore the signature of John Bradbury, Secretary to the Treasury. Treasury notes of various types continued until 1928 when their function was taken over by the Bank of England. Treasury notes lingered on in general circulation until July 1933 when they were called in and ceased to be legal tender.

The traditional white fivers were replaced by notes of a more conventional design in 1957. The subsequent history of Bank of England notes reflects the steady depreciation in the real value of money, through the reduction in the size of notes, the demise of the 10s note in 1970 and the pound note a decade later, as well as the greater prevalence of £10 and £20 notes at the present time. Pound notes survived longer in Scotland and the Isle of Man. Today, only the Royal Bank of Scotland persists with new issues of pound notes, although their average life is reduced to no more than a few months in circulation, and the cost of producing them must now outweigh the benefits of retaining them.

Banknotes in the Rest of the World

The pattern of note-issuing in the rest of the world follows similar lines. In North America, for example, the earliest paper money in Canada consisted of playing cards with handwritten inscriptions, while Massachusetts had notes by December 1690. Although specie was generally preferred there was a rash of paper money in the rebellious colonies during the American Revolutionary War. This set a doubtful precedent for the prolific issues of state banks and countless private banks and even insurance companies in the nineteenth century. The American Civil War produced not only a profligate issue of notes in the Confederacy but various makeshifts on the Union side, ranging from encased postage stamps to fractional currency—small notes which reproduced postage stamps of the appropriate value.

After the Civil War the US government, through the Treasury, continued to release notes of various kinds: Demand Notes, Legal Tender Notes, Compound Interest treasury Notes, Interest Bearing Notes, Silver Certificates, Coin Notes and National Bank Notes. Under the terms of the Federal Reserve Act of 1913 new kinds of currency consisted of Federal Reserve Bank Notes and Federal Reserve Notes, redeemed by the banks and the US government respectively.

Generally speaking, most countries went through a period in which notes were issued by commercial and private banks, followed by legislation to limit or consolidate this practice. By the late-nineteenth century, however, note issues were more generally restricted to a national or state bank, sometimes augmented by lower denominations issued directly by the government, or one of its agencies such as the treasury or finance ministry. These latter issues were often produced in times of financial crisis or war, when there was a shortage of coinage.

In the course of the twentieth century, as people became much more confident in paper and appreciated its convenience over coinage, the range of denominations tended to expand, and notes of even quite low face value became more common. During both world wars paper largely superseded gold and silver coin, and in addition there were special issues by occupying powers for territories under their administration, or military notes prepared in connection with invasion or liberation of enemy-held territory. There were even distinctive notes for prisoner of war, internment and concentration camps. Emergency issues in time of economic crisis or rampant inflation have appeared in Germany, Austria and Poland in the early 1920s, in China, Greece and Hungary in the aftermath of World War II, and, more recently, in Turkey, Poland, Yugoslavia and many parts of Latin America an the former Communist bloc—all yielding an abundance of material for the natophilist to study and collect.

Skit notes

A skit note, or flash note, is a piece of paper which imitates a banknote for various reasons other than to hoodwink the public into thinking they have the genuine article. Many of them have been produced for advertising and sales stunts, while others were intended as satires on politicians and other figures in the public eye. Because they often parodied genuine notes they are of sideline interest in notaphily.

Arguably the most famous skit note of all was that designed by the cartoonist and satirist George Cruikshank as a protest at the draconian laws against counterfeiters. Cruikshank and his friends in the Society of Arts argued that if banks resorted to more complicated printing processes, such as a combination of copperplate engraving and lithography, this would defeat the forger and render notes secure; but so long as many banks relied on letterpress which any half-competent forger could imitate, the temptation would always be there.

Cruikshank designed his Bank Restriction Note which he entered at Stationers' Hall and subsequently retailed at a shilling a time. The note was inscribed "Specimen of a Bank Note— not to be imitated. Submitted to the Consideration of the Bank Directors and the inspection of the Public". The figure of Britannia in the upper left-hand corner parodied the device on genuine Bank of England notes, but she was shown wiping tears from her eyes and eating her baby, surrounded by corpses and skulls. The pound sign was made of a hangman's rope, while the main part of the design showed a gallows on which eleven men and

George Cruishanks "Bank Restriction Note" produced as a protest against counterfeiting laws, 1818.

women were hanging. Above this gruesome picture were the words "Promise to Perform" and underneath was the inscription "During the Issue of Bank Notes easily imitated and until the Resumption of Cash Payments or the Abolition of the Punishment of Death". The note was signed on behalf of the Governor and Company of the Bank of England by Jack Ketch, the notorious public hangman of the period.

As a result of Cruikshank's note, a best-seller which caused rioting on the streets of London, the government was forced to take action. A Royal Commission was appointed in 1818 to investigate ways of producing notes which could not be imitated. Sir Charles Bagot, the British ambassador in Washington, discovered a firm called Murray, Draper, Fairman & Co which had recently adopted several devices that revolutionised banknote printing.

These processes were the invention of Jacob Perkins, an employee of the company, whom Sir Charles induced to come over to London and offer his services to the Bank of England. Perkins was awarded a contract in 1819 and began printing notes by his siderographic process. In this way the great security printing firm of Perkins Bacon had its beginnings, going on to even greater fame and fortune two decades later when they produced the world's first adhesive postage stamps.

Apart from Cruikshank's satirical note, skit notes had their origins in the early 19th century, as a way round the very strict laws governing counterfeits. Apart from the forgers, who automatically went to the gallows for their sins, people passing forgeries of banknotes were liable to transportation for life. A skit note, which did not actually counterfeit the notes of any real bank, avoided the worst penalties of the law. The trick was to get up something that looked like a banknote but was not.

It could be argued that they were produced merely as a form of practical joke, but they were deliberately palmed off on the illiterate or semi-literate people who were induced to accept them at markets and fairs and then found, to their cost, that what they had accepted in payment for goods or services proved to be quite worthless. These notes cannot be regarded as counterfeits though, like Cruikshank's note, they often parodied the designs of existing banknotes.

Such notes purported to be issued by the Bank of Fools (an April Fools' Day joke), or the Bank of Hearts (for giving to one's lover on St Valentine's Day). Others were produced as advertising gimmicks by enterprising tradesmen. The Bank of Perukes, for example, issued skit notes advertising a Liverpool firm of wig-makers.

In the 1870s Thomas Lipton produced notes that parodied the pound notes of the National Bank of Scotland to advertise his groceries. These skit notes, handed out to passers-by in the street, were so close to the originals that many poor illiterate people thought they were genuine. When they tried to spend them they were often arrested and sentenced to varying terms of imprisonment. Lipton himself was severely castigated for this stunt.

Imitation paper money is often used, to this day, for advertisement purposes. The coupons given out by soap manufacturers sometimes have the superficial appearance of banknotes, complete with ornate designs and an intricate geometrical background imitating the engine-turned background of banknotes.

A famous example with numismatic overtones was the £40 note produced in 1977 by the Pobjoy Mint in connection with a buy-back guarantee on Silver Jubilee coins of the Isle of Man. The notes bore the portrait of the Queen and were not unlike the £20 notes of the period in colour. Protests from the Bank of England led to their hurried withdrawal and subsequent "notes" from this mint were clearly marked

VOUCHER and replaced the Queen's portrait by the pound sign and value.

British skit notes in this category are very seldom so well designed and printed and therefore cause no confusion. King Cole's Quids and leaflets advertising local radio stations are good examples of this crude but lively form of advertising.

In this category come imitation notes dropped over enemy territory in time of war. People see a note fluttering to the ground and out of curiosity they rush to pick it up, or they chance upon it on the ground and think they have found the genuine article, but only then do they realise that it is a clever forgery with part of the inscription altered for propaganda purposes. Arguably the most famous of these notes was the British forgery of German Reichsmarks which seemed genuine enough until the finder saw the message on the reverse: "Ich bin Hitlers Arschwisch" intimating that they were, to put it delicately, Der Fuehrer's toilet-paper!

Skit notes are still occasionally used for satirical purposes. In 1966, imitations of British £5 notes were produced in Rhodesia at the height of the UDI controversy. In place of Queen Elizabeth's portrait they showed a caricature of the then British prime minister, Harold Wilson, complete with his pipe, and in place of the usual promise to pay the bearer there was a reference to political promises which had been broken. These notes were crudely printed in black on white paper and would never have deceived anybody, but no doubt they served to boost morale in Rhodesia at the time.

American banknotes have probably been more widely parodied than any others, and range from straightforward advertising gimmicks to pornographic imitations of the greenback. They have been printed in the form of toilet rolls and the rice papers used for rolling a "joint". Satirical versions include the Bucks of the United States of America (sic), the American State of Chance or the notes lampooning the financial guru Warren Buffett.

There are dollars which appear to be genuine, until you turn them over and find religious texts (such as "money is the root of all evil", etc.) or invitations to strip clubs.

Then there are imitations of banknotes which are offered in pads and can be used for jotting down notes and memoranda. Apart from the ubiquitous greenbacks, there are such pads reproducing Scottish banknotes, and very handsome souvenirs they make.

Another sideline of banknotes consists of imitations used in wrapping paper or packaging of various kinds

A modern day Australian skit notes produced for political purposes worth one "Brass Razoo"!

The origin of
Pound notes

POUND NOTES are virtually a thing of the past; only the Royal Bank of Scotland continues to issue them, but for how much longer is doubtful, given their very limited life in general circulation. Although paper money of one sort or another had been in existence since the later 17th century pound notes were a relative latecomer, as the public preferred coins. Not surprisingly, it took a national crisis in the late 18th century to initiate pound notes, and significantly their revival in the early 20th century was also precipitated by an event of cataclysmic proportions...

In 1797, when Britain was at war with Revolutionary France, a rumour circulated that the enemy had landed an expeditionary force on the Welsh coast. As a matter of fact an American adventurer in the French service had led a flotilla of three warships which landed some 600 troops near St David's in Pembrokeshire. This was merely a diversionary tactic, intended to distract the British from the main thrust, which was an invasion of Ireland. The small contingent of French troops, stranded without support or supplies, was soon rounded up by the local militia.

Nevertheless, the invasion of Wales triggered off a nation-wide panic and this led to a run on the banks of such proportions that the gold reserves of the Bank of England were drastically depleted. Such was the shortage of specie that the government issued an Order in Council suspending bank payments in cash until Parliament could consider the situation. The Bank Restriction Act of 1797 gave legal sanction to this draconian measure, and it was not until 1821, long after the Napoleonic Wars, that specie payments were resumed.

In the intervening period, when silver was almost as scarce a commodity as gold, the Bank of England followed the example of the provincial banks and resorted to low-denomination notes for one or two pounds. At the same time, pound notes of the private banks proliferated and, as a consequence, forgery became very common, despite the severe penalties inflicted on those convicted of counterfeiting.

Bank of England one and two pound notes were withdrawn in 1821 when the Bank Restriction Act was repealed, but within a few years immense pressure on gold arose from another quarter. In November 1825 the eminent firm of Sir Peter Pole and Company, London agent for more than 40 provincial banks, failed with a catastrophic knock-on effect. Once more, the public panicked and rushed to convert Bank of England paper into gold. As a result of the gold shortage, the Bank re-issued a stock of 1821 pound notes which, quite by chance, had not been destroyed and still reposed in the vaults. These notes were overprinted with the new date and are thus unique in having two dates, 1821 at the top and 20 December 1825 at the foot. These makeshifts were promptly withdrawn when the gold crisis evaporated a few months later.

It is a fallacy to suppose that there were no pound notes around at this period. In fact it was only the Bank of England which was prevented from issuing such low-denomination notes. The banks in Scotland and Ireland, as well as the country banks of England and Wales, had been issuing notes for a guinea or a pound for many years, but these notes tended to have very limited local circulation. As a result of numerous bank failures, however, the Bank Charter Act of 1844 limited the issue of notes in England and Wales to 72 joint-stock banks and 207 other banks in the provinces. As no bank with offices in London was permitted to issue notes, this regulation rapidly reduced the number, although it was not until 1921 that the last of the country banks to issue pound notes—Fox, Fowler & Company of Wellington, Somerset—gave up this privilege when it amalgamated with Lloyd's Bank.

In addition, there were various attempts, notably by the pioneer of industrial philanthropy, Robert Owen, to produce paper money as part of an experiment in industrial and social economy. In the 1830s Owen produced notes through his National Equitable Labour Exchange, whose headquarters were located in Charlotte Street, Rathbone Place, London, with

A selection of £1 Provincial notes.

branches in Birmingham and other industrial centres. Owen's notes were remarkably elaborate for the period, featuring two vignettes showing a beehive and a pair of scales to symbolise industry and justice or fair-dealing. These notes were unusual in being denominated not in any actual currency but in hours of labour. Thus workers were paid in notes according to the hours they worked, and the notes could then be spent in Exchange stores, goods being given of the requisite value. This was not so very different from the common practice of many factories and collieries in the early years of the Industrial Revolution, whereby workers were paid in vouchers or scrip which could only be redeemed in goods from the company store. This system was open to abuse and was eventually outlawed by the Truck Act of 1840.

In 1891 George Goschen, then Chancellor of the Exchequer, recommended that the Bank of England should resume the issue of pound notes in order to conserve the Bank's gold, but nothing came of the proposal, because the public preferred sovereigns. The general attitude was neatly summed up by a letter to the Referee, a periodical of the 1890s:

Mr Goschen has been considering the one pound notes from various points of view, but there is one aspect of the question he has overlooked, namely the sanitary, and I conclude from this he has never lived, as I have, in a one pound note country. The five pound Bank of England note is a clean crisp wholesome thing, the rustle of which is almost in itself a liberal education. This character the five pound note maintains because it passes through few hands before returning to the Bank, and enjoys what may be called a very select circulation. It is otherwise with the one pound note as known in Scotland and Ireland. Like Wellington's army it goes everywhere and does everything. It is fair to say that the five pound note is handled chiefly by ladies, gentlemen and professional cashiers, but when you produce paper money to the value of twenty shillings there is no hand so dirty but may grasp it. And that is not its worst fate. It is a common thing for Irish navvies and cattle drovers to carry one pound notes in their boots. At any wayside inn in Scotland or Ireland again you may see a dirty ruffian fish out of the lining of his clothes a something

which he will carefully unfold and spread over the counter. When he has done this you see before you a tattered one pound note—the same note that will tomorrow come into your possession. For the one pound note circulates until it falls to pieces, by which time it has absorbed nameless abominations. The people who coined the expression as to money having no smell knew nothing of the one pound note of commerce.

Until the outbreak of war in 1914 the people of Britain had considered themselves singularly exempt from the fears of invasion and the liability to personal military service, which plagued their Continental neighbours. While a professional soldier could be employed to do all the necessary fighting and dying for thirteen pence a day, all the ordinary citizen need do was to read the reports of his doings and supply the criticism, but the days preceding the fateful August 4 hung heavy with sinister portent and the refusal of post offices to change five pound notes brought a conviction of national crisis to the man in the street.

This conviction was emphasised when pound and ten-shilling notes, crudely printed in red and black, were issued by the Treasury. The makeshift nature of these notes has been offered in evidence that Britain was innocent of any premeditation of entering the war, and when one compares these early Treasury notes with the one-mark notes issued by the German government at this period, one can see that this argument carries considerable weight. Later issues were better in design and production, and were then replaced by a more colourful form of Treasury note which was certainly more like a banknote than a coupon cut from a newspaper.

After 1914 there was to be no reversion to gold coins in general circulation. Notes of relatively small denominations were here to stay. Only the relentless march of inflation since the 1960s would ensure the demise, first of the ten-shilling note, and then of the pound. And now it can only be a matter of time before the five pound note, the prerogative of the professional classes a century ago but now reduced in size, status and active life, goes the same way and becomes a thing of the past.

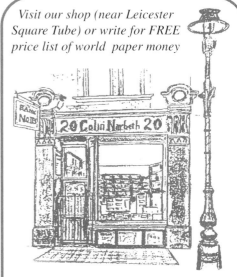

PRICE GUIDE
to the banknotes of England, Scotland, Channel Islands, the Isle of Man and Ireland

The price one should pay for a banknote can vary depending on a whole variety of criteria. In this price guide the figures given are intended as a *guide only* to prices that one should expect to pay for notes in the condition noted at the top of each column—the grading is as explained in the grading table on page 25. Notes in lower grades would obviously cost far less and notes in exceptional condition can command higher prices than those given. The notes listed are ordinary circulating examples.

To comply with current legislation illustrations of all modern notes have been endorsed with the word SPECIMEN—this, of course, does not appear on the notes themselves. Proofs, specimen printings and other varieties are beyond the scope of this publication—for further information the reader is referred to the relevant specialist book as listed in the Bibliography on pages 211–215.

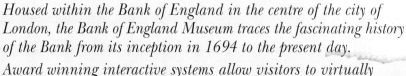

EARLY BANK OF ENGLAND NOTES

By the close of the 17th century London was becoming one of the most important trading and commercial centres of the world. Its rich merchants and goldsmiths, many of whom are remembered to this day in the names of the banks such as Martins, Lloyds, Barclays and Glyn Mills, had been issuing promissory notes and receipts for valuables for many years and these pieces of paper were accepted as if they were actually money. By 1680 there were about fifty of these merchants whose promissory notes were readily acceptable. With the rapid development of England as a trading nation it became necessary to establish some sort of national bank. In 1694, the Bank of England was founded by William Paterson, a Scotsman whose proposals were readily endorsed by Charles Montagu, the Chancellor of the Exchequer at the time. In the year of its foundation the Bank issued only a few notes, for £20 and £50, and these were entirely hand-written like the merchants' notes.

The first printed notes were released on June 5, 1695 but had a very short life, being hurriedly withdrawn when a cunning forger obtained a quantity of paper from the same supplier as the Bank and then produced excellent counterfeits. The Bank got around this problem by using a different type of paper, with a marbled pattern. As a further precaution against fraud, these marbled notes were cut in half and only one half given to the customer. When the note came back to the bank it could be checked against the other half to prove that it was genuine. None of these marbled notes has survived, but the practice of cutting notes in half continued for some time. Later notes may be found with curved cuts between the two halves as well as a printed design.

A watermark was adopted as a security feature in 1697 and specially watermarked paper has been used for all Bank of England notes since then. The notes from 1696 to 1725 had the amounts written in by hand and could be issued for any odd amount from £10 upwards. Regular denominations were re-introduced in 1725 and were issued in values from £20 to £1000. In 1759 notes for £10 and £15 were added, and six years later a £25 was introduced. The Bank of England did not issue notes of lower value, and it was left to the many private banks to fill the gap. The first £5 notes appeared in 1793, a year when many private banks crashed as a result of the outbreak of war with Revolutionary France.

During a shortage of gold coin during the Napoleonic Wars, notes of £1 and £2 were added to the series and these continued until 1829, but thereafter the Bank reverted to notes from £5 to £1000 only. All of these 19th century notes are of the greatest rarity. They are generally grouped according to the signature of the Chief Cashier which appears on them. At various times from 1826 onwards branches of the Bank of England were opened in a number of provincial cities, resulting in notes specifically inscribed. For full details of the early notes consult *English Paper Money* by Vincent Duggleby. Our listing of Bank of England notes is confined to the period from 1902 onwards at which point examples of most denominations become available in collectable condition, although even then the higher values, £500 and £1000 (which ceased in 1943), are of considerable rarity. Also listed are the notes issued by the Treasury which were issued following the outbreak of World War I. The Bank of England, at that time was only empowered to issue notes of £5 and over and due to the predicted restrictions on gold, Treasury notes were issued in denominations of ten shillings and one pound with the intention of replacing the sovereign and half sovereign.

All the notes listed are printed, in black or coloured ink as indicated, on white paper.

TREASURY NOTES

Notes of one shilling (1/–), two shillings and sixpence (2/6) and five shillings (5/–) denominations, signed by John Bradbury, were produced in November 1919 but were never issued. However, a few examples survived and somehow escaped and very occasionally come onto the market and command very high prices.

	VF	EF

TEN SHILLINGS

First Bradbury issue 10/–.

FIRST (EMERGENCY) BRADBURY ISSUE (August 1914)

Red. 127 x 63mm. Blank reverse
Signature: John Bradbury

	VF	EF
Prefix A. *No* followed by Letter over number followed by 6 serial numbers	£250	£500
Prefix A–Z (various). Letter over number followed by *No*. and 5 or 6 serial numbers	£450	£800

SECOND BRADBURY ISSUE (January 1915)
Red. 136 x 76mm.
Signature: John Bradbury

	VF	EF
Prefix A–Z. Letter over number followed by 5 serial numbers	£100	£250
Prefix N–Z. Letter over number followed by 6 serial numbers	£150	£500

"DARDANELLES" OVERPRINT on above

"Dardanelles" overprint on Second Bradbury issue.

Overprinted in Arabic for the use of the British Expeditionary Forces in Turkey in 1915

	VF	EF
Prefix Y or Z. Letter over number followed by 6 serial numbers	£400	£900

VF   *EF*

Third Bradbury issue 10/–

THIRD BRADBURY ISSUE (October 1918)
Green, brown and purple. 138 x 78mm
Signature: John Bradbury

	VF	EF
Prefix A. Letter over number followed by *No.* and serial numbers	£200	£350
Prefix A. Letter over number followed by *No* and serial numbers	£150	£300

(December 1919)

	VF	EF
Prefix B or C. Letter over number followed by *No.* and serial numbers in red	£800	£1500
Prefix B or C. Letter over number followed by *No* and serial numbers in red	£150	£300

FIRST FISHER ISSUE (September 1919)
Brown, green and purple. 138 x 78mm
Signature N. F. Warren Fisher

	VF	EF
Prefix D–H. Letter over number followed by *No.* and serial numbers ..	£50	£150
Prefix D–H. Letter over number followed by *No* and serial numbers ...	£45	£120

SECOND FISHER ISSUE (November 1922)

Second Fisher issue 10/–

Brown, green and purple. 138 x 78mm
Signature N. F. Warren Fisher

	VF	EF
Prefix J–S. Letter over number followed by serial numbers	£45	£75

THIRD FISHER ISSUE (July 1927) ("NORTHERN" ADDED TO TITLE)
Brown, green and purple. 138 x 78mm
Signature N. F. Warren Fisher

	VF	EF
Prefix S–U, W. Letter over number followed by serial numbers	£50	£150

VF   EF

Third Bradbury issue £1.

ONE POUND

FIRST (EMERGENCY) BRADBURY ISSUE (August 1914)

Black. 127 x 63mm. Blank reverse
Signature: John Bradbury
Prefix A, B, or C .... from £700   from £1500
Prefix A–Z. Letter over number followed by *No.* or *N̲o̲* and serial
number .... from £250   from £500
Prefix BB–LL. Double letter over number followed by *No.* and serial
numbers .... from £300   from £600

SECOND BRADBURY ISSUE (January 1915)
Black. 136 x 76mm.
Signature: John Bradbury
Prefix A–Z. Letter over number followed by 5 serial numbers £150   £450

"DARDANELLES" OVERPRINT
Overprinted in Arabic for the use of the British Expeditionary Forces in 1915
Prefix F, J, M, Y. Letter over number followed by 5 serial numbers £1250   £2750

THIRD BRADBURY ISSUE (January 1917)
Green, brown and purple. 151 x 84mm. Blank reverse
Signature: John Bradbury
Prefix A. Letter over number followed by serial numbers £100   £250
Prefix B–H. Letter over number followed by serial numbers £75   £100
Prefix Z. Letter over number followed by serial numbers £75   £100

FIRST FISHER ISSUE (September 1919)
Brown, green and purple. 152 x 85mm
Signature N. F. Warren Fisher
Prefix K–Z. Letter over number followed by *No.* and serial numbers ... £30   £65

SECOND FISHER ISSUE (November 1922)
Brown, green and purple. 152 x 85mm
Signature N. F. Warren Fisher
Prefix B1–R1. Letter over number followed by *No.* and serial numbers   £45   £75
— *No.* with square dot below £75   £150
Prefix A1, Z1. Letter over number followed by *No.* and serial numbers   £50   £85

THIRD FISHER ISSUE (July 1927) ("NORTHERN" ADDED TO TITLE)
Brown, green and purple. 152 x 85mm
Signature N. F. Warren Fisher
Prefix S1–X1. Letter over number followed by *No.* and serial numbers   £70   £130
— *No.* with square dot below £75   £150
Prefix Z1. Letter over number followed by *No.* and serial numbers £70   £125

BANK OF ENGLAND
1902–28

Most of the "White" notes were also issued at branch offices in Birmingham, Bristol, Hull, Leeds, Liverpool, Manchester, Newcastle, Plymouth and Portsmouth. Very few examples of the 19th century issues of these exist today. When available in most cases they command a considerable premium.

These notes were all printed in black on white paper in sheets of four which were then cut up to give one straight edge and three uncut (deckled) edges. They are commonly referred to as "White" notes.

Later issues of the famous "White" notes are found under "Bank of England issues from 1928".

	VF	EF

FIVE POUNDS

(1902)
Signature: J. G. Nairne
London £150 £300

(1918)
Signature: E. M. Harvey
London £100 £175

TEN POUNDS

(1902)
Signature: J. G. Nairne
London £300 £500

(1918)
Signature: E. M. Harvey
London £150 £250

	VF	EF

TWENTY POUNDS

(1902)
Signature: J. G. Nairne
London £1000   £2000

(1918)
Signature: E. M. Harvey
London £500   £1000

FIFTY POUNDS

(1902)
Signature: J. G. Nairne
London £1500   £2500

(1918)
Signature: E. M. Harvey
London £400   £1000

ONE HUNDRED POUNDS

(1902)
Signature: J. G. Nairne
London .... £2000   £3000+

(1918)
Signature: E. M. Harvey
London £800   £1500

One pound no. 4—one of the earliest known Bank of England notes, dated 1797.

BANK OF ENGLAND
From 1928

In these listings the known prefix letters are given and the corresponding valuations
are for *mid-range* notes. It must be emphasised that first and last notes of a series are worth a
considerable premium and many are never seen on the market. Where the first and the last prefixes
are known these have been included but *not* usually priced.

TEN SHILLINGS

BRITANNIA ISSUE

	VF	EF
(November 1928)		
Red-brown. 140 x 78mm		
Signature: C. P. Mahon		
Prefix sequence: Letter/Number/Number		
Prefix A01 followed by serial number	£350	£600
Prefix Z - -	£50	£100
Prefix W - -, X - -, Y - -	£50	£90
Prefix V - -	£125	£250
(July 1930)		
Red-brown. 140 x 78mm		
Signature: B. G. Catterns		
Prefix sequence: Letter/Number/Number		
Prefix V - - followed by serial number	£50	£100
Prefix L - - to U - -	£35	£60
Prefix K - -	£40	£70
(October 1934)		
Red-brown. 140 x 78mm		
Signature: K. O. Peppiatt		
Prefix sequence: Letter/Number/Number		
Prefix J - - followed by serial number	£30	£70
Prefix H - - to B - -	£15	£35
Prefix A - -	£30	£70
Prefix sequence: Number/Number/Letter		
Prefix - - Z	£25	£60
Prefix - - Y to - - R	£20	£50
Prefix - - O	£45	£100

Ten shillings Britannia issue (continued)   VF   EF

(March 1940)

Mauve. 140 x 78mm. With metal security thread
Signature: K. O. Peppiatt
Prefix sequence: Letter/Number/Number/Letter

Prefix Z01D	£60	£175
Prefix Z - - D	£15	£30
Prefix Y - - D to B - - D	£12	£25
Prefix A - - D	£15	£35
Prefix Z - - E, Y - - E	£18	£40
Prefix X - - E (X21E last seen)	£30	£65

(June 1948)

Red-brown. 140 x 78mm. Without metal security thread
Signature: K. O. Peppiatt
Prefix sequence: Number/Number/Letter

Prefix - - L followed by serial number	£45	£100

(October 1948)

Red-brown. 140 x 78mm. With metal security thread
Signature: K. O. Peppiatt
Prefix sequence: Number/Number/Letter

Prefix - - L followed by serial number	£45	£90
Prefix - - H, - - J, - - K	£12	£25
Prefix - - E	£10	£30
Prefix 01A–03A (Replacement note)	£350	£500

(March 1950)

Red-brown. 140 x 78mm.
Signature: P. S. Beale
Prefix sequence: Number/Number/Letter

Prefix - - E followed by serial number	£40	£95
Prefix - - D, - - C	£12	£25
Prefix - - B	£15	£35

Prefix sequence: Letter/Number/Number/Letter

Prefix Z - - Z followed by serial number	£10	£35
Prefix Y - - Z to E - - Z	£10	£25
Prefix D - - Z	£15	£35

Prefix sequence: Number/Number/Letter

Prefix - - A (04A first and 35A last)	£30	£65

(November 1955)

Red-brown. 140 x 78mm.
Signature: L. K. O'Brien
Prefix sequence: Letter/Number/Number/Letter

Prefix D - - Z followed by serial number (D86Z first)	£15	£35
Prefix C - - Z, B - - Z	£6	£15
Prefix A - - Z (A99Z last)	£8	£20
Prefix Z01Y	£30	£80
Prefix Z - - Y	£7	£18
Prefix Y - - Y to B - - Y	£6	£15
Prefix A - - Y (A99Y last)	£8	£20
Prefix Z01X	£30	£80
Prefix Y - - X	£10	£20
Prefix Y25X last	£35	£90
Prefix - - A (Replacement notes) (36A first and 69A last)	£18	£55

Ten shillings (continued)

ROYAL PORTRAIT ISSUE

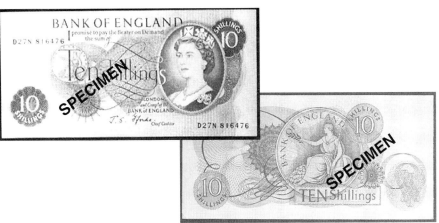

	EF	UNC
(April 1963)		

Red-brown. 140 x 66.7mm.
Signature: L. K. O'Brien
Prefix sequence: Letter/Number/Number

	EF	UNC
Prefix A01	£20	£50
Prefix A - - followed by serial number	£5	£10
Prefix B - - to J - -	£2	£5
Prefix K - - (K64 last)	£5	£10
Prefix M - - (Replacement note) (M01 first and M18 last)	£8	£20

Signature: J. Q. Hollom
Prefix sequence: Letter/Number/Number

	EF	UNC
Prefix K - - followed by serial number	£5	£10
Prefix K65	£40	£100
Prefix L - - to Y - -	£2	£5
Prefix Z - - (Z99 last)	£5	£20
Prefix M - - (Replacement note) (M19 first and M55 last)	£8	£20

Prefix sequence: Number/Number/Letter

	EF	UNC
Prefix - - A followed by serial number	£5	£15
Prefix - - B to - - N	£2	£5
Prefix - - R (01A first and 26R last)	£8	£15

(February 1967)

Red-brown. 140 x 66.7mm.
Signature: J. S. Fforde
Prefix sequence: Letter/Number/Number

	EF	UNC
Prefix - - R followed by serial number	£5	£12
Prefix - - S to - - Y	£2	£7
Prefix - - Z	£2	£10

Prefix sequence: Letter/Number/Number/Letter

	EF	UNC
Prefix A - - N followed by serial number	£2	£8
Prefix B - - N, C - - N	£2	£5
Prefix D - - N (D38N exists)	£2	£7
Prefix M - - (Replacement note) (M56 first and M80 last)	£10	£20

ONE POUND

BRITANNIA ISSUE

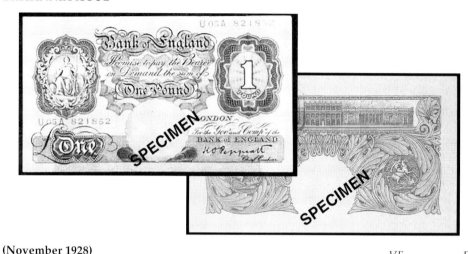

(November 1928)

	VF	EF

Green. 151 x 85mm
Signature: C. P. Mahon
Prefix sequence: Letter/Number/Number

	VF	EF
Prefix A01 followed by serial number	£250	£450
Prefix A - -	£50	£100
Prefix B - - to G - -	£25	£75
Prefix H - - (H32 last)	£75	£150
Presentation set of Ten shilling and One pound notes with matching serial numbers in special Bank of England parchment envelope		£4000

(July 1930)

Green. 151 x 85mm
Signature: B. G. Catterns
Prefix sequence: Letter/Number/Number

	VF	EF
Prefix H - - followed by serial number (H35 first)	£30	£75
Prefix J - - to Z - - (Z99 last)	£18	£25

Prefix sequence: Number/Number/Letter

	VF	EF
Prefix - - A (01A first and 99A last)	£40	£75

(October 1934)

Green. 151 x 85mm
Signature: K. O. Peppiatt
Prefix sequence: Number/Number/Letter

	VF	EF
Prefix - - B followed by serial number (03B first)	£25	£50
Prefix - - C to - - Y	£15	£25
Prefix - - Z (99Z last)	£20	£35

Prefix sequence: Letter/Number/Number/Letter

	VF	EF
Prefix A - - A followed by serial number (A03A first, *A01A, A02A not seen*)	£15	£25
Prefix B - - A to K - - A	£10	£20
Prefix L - - A (L39A last)	£12	£20

(March 1940)

Blue (various shades). 151 x 85mm. With metal security thread
Signature: K. O. Peppiatt
Prefix sequence: Letter/Number/Number/Letter

	VF	EF
Prefix A - - D followed by serial number (A01D first, A99D last)	£8	£19

One pound Britannia issue (continued)	*VF*	*EF*

(March 1940) *(continued)*

	VF	EF
Prefix A - - E (A01E first, A99E last)	£8	£19
Prefix A - - H (A01H first, A99H last)	£8	£19
Prefix B - - D (B01D first), B - - E (B01E first), B - - H (B01H first)	£10	£20
Prefix Z - - D (Z87D last, probably exists up to Z99D),		
W - - E (W48E last), X - - H (X96H last)	£10	£20
Prefix C - - D to Y - - D, C - - E to U - - E, C - - H to W - - H	£3	£8
Prefix Z - - D, W - - E, X - - H	£15	£25

(June 1948)

Green. 151 x 85mm. Without metal security thread
Signature: K. O. Peppiatt
Prefix sequence: Letter/Number/Number/Letter

	VF	EF
Prefix R - - A followed by serial number (R01A first, R99A last)	£8	£15
Prefix S - - A (S01A first, S48A last) overlaps exist with threaded series	£14	£30

(September 1948)

Green. 151 x 85mm. With metal security thread
Signature: K. O. Peppiatt
Prefix sequence: Letter/Number/Number/Letter

	VF	EF
Prefix S - - A followed by serial number (S39A first)	£25	£75
Prefix T - - A to Y - - A	£12	£25
Prefix Z - - A (Z99A last)	£15	£25
Prefix A - - B (A01B first)	£12	£25
Prefix B - - B to E - - B	£10	£20
Prefix H - - B (H36B last)	£20	£50
Prefix S - - S (Replacement note) (S01S first, S09S last)	£80	£200

(March 1950)

Green. 151 x 85mm.
Signature: P. S. Beale
Prefix sequence: Letter/Number/Number/Letter

	VF	EF
Prefix H - - B followed by serial number (H37B first)	£8	£18
Prefix J - - B to Y - - B	£3	£5
Prefix Z - - B (Z99B last)	£8	£18
Prefix A - -C (A01C first)	£8	£18
Prefix B - - C to Y - - C	£3	£5
Prefix Z - - C (Z99C last)	£8	£18
Prefix A - - J (A01J first)	£8	£18
Prefix B - -J to K - -J	£3	£5
Prefix L - - J (L63J last)	£8	£18
Prefix S - - S (Replacement notes) (S10S first, S70S last)	£15	£30

(November 1955)

Green. 151 x 85mm.
Signature: L. K. O'Brien
Prefix sequence: Letter/Number/Number/Letter

	VF	EF
Prefix L - - J followed by serial number (L64J first)..............................	£6	£12
Prefix M - - J to Y - - J	£3	£6
Prefix Z - - J (Z99J last)	£5	£10
Prefix A - - K (A01K first)	£6	£12
Prefix B - - K to Y - - K	£3	£6
Prefix Z - - K (Z99K last)	£6	£12
Prefix A - - L (A02L first)	£6	£12
Prefix B - - L to J - - L..	£3	£6
Prefix K - - L (K13L last)	£15	£35
Prefix S - - S (Replacement note) (S71Sfirst, S99S last)	£12	£25
Prefix S - - T(Replacement note) (S01T first, 23T last)	£15	£40

One pound (continued)

ROYAL PORTRAIT ISSUE

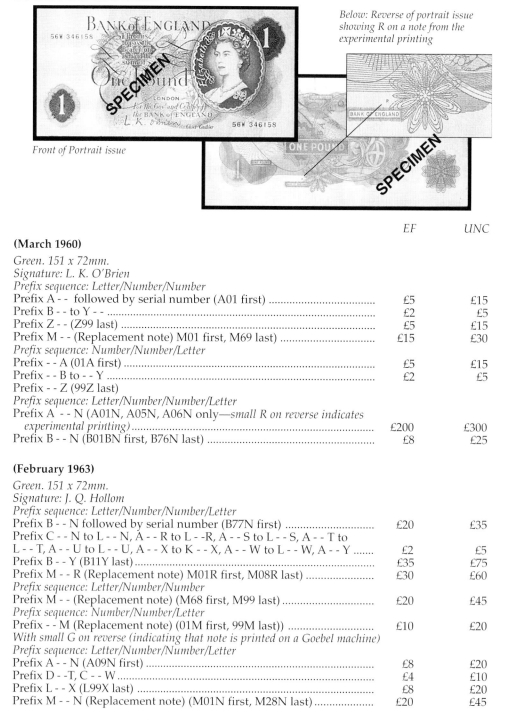

Below: Reverse of portrait issue showing R on a note from the experimental printing

Front of Portrait issue

	EF	UNC

(March 1960)

Green. 151 x 72mm.
Signature: L. K. O'Brien
Prefix sequence: Letter/Number/Number

	EF	UNC
Prefix A - - followed by serial number (A01 first)	£5	£15
Prefix B - - to Y - -	£2	£5
Prefix Z - - (Z99 last)	£5	£15
Prefix M - - (Replacement note) M01 first, M69 last	£15	£30

Prefix sequence: Number/Number/Letter

	EF	UNC
Prefix - - A (01A first)	£5	£15
Prefix - - B to - - Y	£2	£5
Prefix - - Z (99Z last)		

Prefix sequence: Letter/Number/Number/Letter

	EF	UNC
Prefix A - - N (A01N, A05N, A06N only—*small R on reverse indicates experimental printing*)	£200	£300
Prefix B - - N (B01BN first, B76N last)	£8	£25

(February 1963)

Green. 151 x 72mm.
Signature: J. Q. Hollom
Prefix sequence: Letter/Number/Number/Letter

	EF	UNC
Prefix B - - N followed by serial number (B77N first)	£20	£35
Prefix C - - N to L - - N, A - - R to L - -R, A - - S to L - -S, A - - T to L - - T, A - - U to L - - U, A - - X to K - - X, A - - W to L - - W, A - - Y	£2	£5
Prefix B - - Y (B11Y last)	£35	£75
Prefix M - - R (Replacement note) M01R first, M08R last	£30	£60

Prefix sequence: Letter/Number/Number

	EF	UNC
Prefix M - - (Replacement note) (M68 first, M99 last)	£20	£45

Prefix sequence: Number/Number/Letter

	EF	UNC
Prefix - - M (Replacement note) (01M first, 99M last))	£10	£20

With small G on reverse (indicating that note is printed on a Goebel machine)
Prefix sequence: Letter/Number/Number/Letter

	EF	UNC
Prefix A - - N (A09N first)	£8	£20
Prefix D - -T, C - - W	£4	£10
Prefix L - - X (L99X last)	£8	£20
Prefix M - - N (Replacement note) (M01N first, M28N last)	£20	£45

One pound Royal portrait issue (continued)   EF   UNC

(February 1967)

Green. 151 x 72mm.
Signature: J. S. Fforde
Prefix sequence: Letter/Number/Number/Letter

	EF	UNC
Prefix B - - Y followed by serial number (B11Y first)	£15	£35
Prefix C - - Y to L - - Y, A - - Z to J - - Z	£2	£5
Prefix L - - Z (L99Z last)	£15	£35
Prefix M - - R (Replacement note) (M09R first, M49R last)	£18	£40
Prefix N - - A (N01A first)	£25	£50
Prefix N - - B to N - - L, R - - A to R - - K, S - - A to S - - L, T - - A to T - - L, U - - A to U - - H, W - - A to W - - C, X - - B	£2	£5
Prefix X - - C (X42C last)	£20	£45
Prefix R - - M, S - - M (Replacement note)	£10	£25
Prefix T01M to T04M, U01M (Replacement note)	—	—

With small G on reverse (indicating that note is printed on a Goebel machine)

	EF	UNC
Prefix E - - Y (E01Y first, E99Y last)	£4	£10
Prefix K - - Z (K01Z first, K99Z last)	£4	£10
Prefix M - - N (Replacement note) (M29N first, M42N last)	£18	£40
Prefix R - - B (R01B first, R99B last)	£4	£10
Prefix R - - L (R01L first, R99L last)	£4	£10
Prefix U - - E (U01E first, U45E last)	£4	£10
Prefix N - - M (Replacement note) (N01M first, N14M last)	£20	£40
Prefix T - - M (Replacement note) (T29M first, T32M last)	£75	£170

(1971)

Green. 151 x 72mm.
Signature: J. B. Page
Prefix sequence: Letter/Number/Number/Letter

	EF	UNC
Prefix S - - L followed by serial number (S87L, S89L, S90L only seen) ..	—	—
Prefix S - - M (Replacement note) (S32M first, S99M last)	£10	£20
Prefix T - - B to T - - L, U - - A to U - - H, W - - A to W - - H (T01B first, W99H last)	£2	£4
Prefix X - - A to X - - L, Y - - A to Y - - L, Z - - A to Z - - K (X01A first)..	£2	£4
Prefix Z - - L (Z84L last)	£8	£15
Prefix R - - M (Replacement notes) (R44M first, R99M last)	£10	£25
Prefix W - - M (W01M first, W84M last)	£5	£10
Prefix X - - M (X01M first, X60M last)	£10	£25

Prefix sequence: Letter/Letter/Number/Number

	EF	UNC
Prefix AN - - (AN01 first)	£3	£10
Prefix AR - - to AZ - - , BN - - to BZ - - ,CN - - to CZ - - ,DN - - to DZ - - , EN - - to EZ - - , HN - - to HY - -	£2	£5
Prefix HZ - - (HZ63 last)	£3	£6
Prefix MR - - (Replacement notes) (MR01 first, MR48 last)	£5	£15
Prefix MS - - (Replacement notes) (MS01 first, MS84 last)	£5	£15
Prefix MT - - (Replacement notes) (MT01 first, MT21 last)	£5	£15
Prefix MU - - (Replacement notes) (MU01 first, MU19 last)	£5	£15
Prefix MW - - (Replacement notes) (MW01 first, MW19 last)	£5	£15

For thousands of British and World Banknotes
Visit: www.collectbanknotes.co.uk

One pound (continued)

PICTORIAL ISSUE—SIR ISAAC NEWTON REVERSE

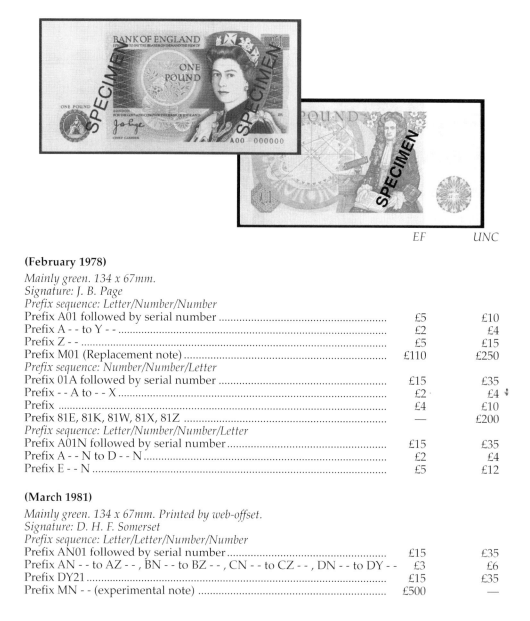

	EF	UNC

(February 1978)

Mainly green. 134 x 67mm.
Signature: J. B. Page
Prefix sequence: Letter/Number/Number

	EF	UNC
Prefix A01 followed by serial number	£5	£10
Prefix A - - to Y - -	£2	£4
Prefix Z - -	£5	£15
Prefix M01 (Replacement note)	£110	£250
Prefix sequence: Number/Number/Letter		
Prefix 01A followed by serial number	£15	£35
Prefix - - A to - - X	£2	£4
Prefix	£4	£10
Prefix 81E, 81K, 81W, 81X, 81Z	—	£200
Prefix sequence: Letter/Number/Number/Letter		
Prefix A01N followed by serial number	£15	£35
Prefix A - - N to D - - N	£2	£4
Prefix E - - N	£5	£12

(March 1981)

Mainly green. 134 x 67mm. Printed by web-offset.
Signature: D. H. F. Somerset
Prefix sequence: Letter/Letter/Number/Number

	EF	UNC
Prefix AN01 followed by serial number	£15	£35
Prefix AN - - to AZ - - , BN - - to BZ - - , CN - - to CZ - - , DN - - to DY - -	£3	£6
Prefix DY21	£15	£35
Prefix MN - - (experimental note)	£500	—

FIVE POUNDS

BLACK AND WHITE SERIES (continued)

	VF	EF
(1925–29)		
Signature: C. P. Mahon		
London	£100	£200
(March 1929)		
Signature: B. G. Catterns		
London	£100	£230
(1934)		
Signature: K. O. Peppiatt		
London	£50	£150
(1945) .		
Incorporating metal security strip. Thick paper		
Signature: K. O. Peppiatt		
Prefix sequence: Letter/Number/Number		
Prefix E - -, H - - to L - - followed by serial number	£50	£95
(1948)		
Signature: K. O. Peppiatt		
Prefix sequence: Letter/Number/Number		
Prefix L - - followed by serial number	£50	£95
Prefix M - -	£50	£100
(1949)		
Signature: P. S. Beale		
Prefix sequence: Letter/Number/Number		
Prefix M - - followed by serial number	£50	£95
Prefix N - - to X - -	£45	£85
Prefix Y - -	£50	£95

Five pounds Black and White series(continued)	*VF*	*EF*

(1955)

Signature: L. K. O'Brien
Prefix sequence: Letter/Number/Number

Prefix Y - - or Z - - followed by serial number	£50	£95

Prefix sequence: Letter/Number/Number/Letter

Prefix A - - A followed by serial number	£45	£95
Prefix B - - A, C - - A	£40	£85
Prefix D - - A	£50	£95

HELMETED BRITANNIA SERIES

	EF	*UNC*
(February 1957)		

Green, blue and orange. Reverse £5 symbol shaded. 159 x 89mm
Signature: L. K. O'Brien
Prefix sequence: Letter/Number/Number

Prefix A - - followed by serial number	£20	£45
Prefix B - - to D - -	£15	£35
Prefix E - -	£20	£45

(July 1961)

Green, blue and orange. Reverse £5 symbol in outline only. 159 x 89mm
Signature: L. K. O'Brien
Prefix sequence: Letter/Number/Number

Prefix H - - followed by serial number	£20	£45
Prefix B - - to J - -	£15	£35
Prefix K - -	£20	£45

Five pounds (continued)   *EF*   *UNC*

ROYAL PORTRAIT SERIES

(February 1963)

Blue. 140 x 85mm
Signature: J. Q. Hollom
Prefix sequence: Letter/Number/Number

	EF	UNC
Prefix A01 followed by serial number	£15	£30
Prefix B - - to N - -	£10	£25
Prefix R - - (R19 last)	£20	£50
Prefix M - - (Replacement note)	£100	£200

(January 1967)

Blue. 140 x 85mm
Signature: J. S. Fforde
Prefix sequence: Letter/Number/Number

	EF	UNC
Prefix R - - followed by serial number (R20 first)	£20	£35
Prefix S - - to Y - -	£10	£20
Prefix Z - - (Z99 last)	£10	£25
Prefix M - - (Replacement note)	£60	£120

Signature: J. B. Page
Prefix sequence: Number/Number/Letter

	EF	UNC
Prefix - - A followed by serial number	£10	£30
Prefix - - B to - - K	£10	£20
Prefix - - L	£20	£35
Prefix - - M (Replacement note)	£60	£140

Five pounds (continued)

PICTORIAL SERIES

	EF	UNC
(November 1971)		

Predominantly blue. 146 x 76mm
Signature: J. B. Page
Prefix sequence: Letter/Number/Number

	EF	UNC
Prefix A01 followed by serial number	£80	£150
Prefix A - - to K - -	£15	£30
Prefix L - - (L94 last)	£50	£100
Prefix M - - (Replacement note)	£50	£140

(August 1973)

Predominantly blue. 146 x 76mm
Signature: J. B. Page
Prefix sequence: Number/Number/Letter

	EF	UNC
Prefix 01A followed by serial number	£80	£160
Prefix - - A to - - Y	£10	£20
Prefix - - Z	£12	£30
Prefix - - M - - (Replacement note)	£50	£130

Prefix sequence: Letter/Letter/Number/Number

	EF	UNC
Prefix AN01	£80	£160
Prefix AN - - to CX - -	£10	£20
Prefix EZ - - (EZ56 last)	£30	£80

(June 1980)

Predominantly blue. With 0.5mm wide security thread. Printed by lithography indicated by small "L"
on reverse. 146 x 76mm
Signature: D. H. F. Somerset
Prefix sequence: Letter/Letter/Number/Number

	EF	UNC
Prefix DN01 followed by serial number	£50	£130
Prefix DN - - to LZ - -	£7	£20
Prefix NA - -	—	—
Prefix NB - - to NC - -	£10	£25

Prefix - - 91, BR91, CS91, DT91, EU91, HW91, JX91, KY91, LZ91 (experimental notes for Optical Character Recognition) normally only seen in VF . £350 —

Five pounds Pictorial series (continued)   *EF*   *UNC*

(July 1987)

Predominantly blue. With 1mm wide security thread. Printed by web offset. 146 x 76mm
Signature: D. H. F. Somerset
Prefix sequence: Letter/Letter/Number/Number

	EF	UNC
Prefix RA01 followed by serial number	£15	£35
Prefix RA - - to RC - -	£10	£18

(March 1988)

Predominantly blue. With 1mm wide security thread. Printed by web offset. 146 x 76mm
Signature: G. M. Gill
Prefix sequence: Letter/Letter/Number/Number

	EF	UNC
Prefix RD01 followed by serial number	£15	£40
Prefix RD - - to RL - -, SA - - to SE - -	£10	£20
Prefix SE90	£30	£85

Five pounds (continued)

HISTORICAL SERIES

(June 1990)   *EF*   *UNC*

Predominantly turquoise. With windowed security thread. 135 x 70mm
Signature: G. M. Gill
Prefix sequence: Letter/Number/Number
Prefix A01 followed by serial number £10   £20
Prefix A - - to U - - £6   £12
Collector's packs including notes with first prefix (A01) of the Historical series and last prefix
(SE90) of the Pictorial series numbered from 998501 to 999999.

(November 1991)

Predominantly turquoise. 135 x 70mm
Signature: G. E. A. Kentfield
Prefix sequence: Letter/Number/Number
Prefix R01 followed by serial number £12   £25
Prefix R - - to W - - (W18 last) £6   £10

(March 1993)

Predominantly turquoise but darker printing than previous. Printed by web offset. 135 x 70mm
Signature: G. E. A. Kentfield
Prefix sequence: Letter/Letter/Number/Number
Prefix AA01 followed by serial number ....   —   £20
Prefix AA - -, AB - - ....   —   £10
Collector's folders contained three uncut notes from the last web offset printing with prefix AB16/
AB17/AB18 numbered from 998501 to 999999.
Printed by sheet fed offset litho
Prefix AC01 followed by serial number ....   —   £95
Prefix AC - - to AE - -, AH - - to AZ - -, BA - - to BJ - -, DA - - to DJ - - ..   —   £10
Collector's folders contained three uncut notes from the first sheet fed printing with prefix AC01/
AC02/AC03 numbered from 0000001 to 001500.

(1999)

Predominantly turquoise. 135 x 70mm
Signature: Merlyn Lowther
Prefix sequence: Letter/Letter/Number/Number
Prefix EA01 followed by serial number ....   —   £20
Prefix EA - - to - - - - ....   —   —

TEN POUNDS

BLACK AND WHITE SERIES (continued)

	VF	EF
(1925–29)		
Signature: C. P. Mahon		
London	£150	£300
(March 1929)		
Signature: B. G. Catterns		
London	£120	£300
(1934)		
Signature: K. O. Peppiatt		
London	£100	£250

Ms Merlyn Lowther who became Chief Cashier at the Bank of England and signatory on the banknotes when Graham Kentfield retired in 1999.

Ten pounds (continued)

ROYAL PORTRAIT SERIES

	EF	*UNC*
(February 1964)		

Brown. 150 x 93mm
Signature: J. Q. Hollom
Prefix sequence: Letter/Number/Number
Prefix A - - followed by serial number (A01 first, A40 last) .... £20 — £35

(January 1967)

Brown. 150 x 93mm
Signature: J. S. Fforde
Prefix sequence: Letter/Number/Number
Prefix A - - followed by serial number (A41 first, A95 last) .... £25 — £45

(1971)

Brown. 150 x 93mm
Signature: J. B. Page
Prefix sequence: Letter/Number/Number
Prefix A - - followed by serial number .... — — —
Prefix B - -, C - - .... £20 — £35
Prefix M - - (Replacement note) .... £25 — £50

Ten pounds (continued)   EF   UNC

PICTORIAL SERIES

(February 1975)

Predominantly brown. 151 x 85mm
Signature: J. B. Page
Prefix sequence: Letter/Number/Number

	EF	UNC
Prefix A - - to T - - followed by serial number	£20	£35
Prefix M - - (Replacement note)	£60	£150

(December 1980)

Predominantly brown. 151 x 85mm
Signature: D. H. F. Somerset
Prefix sequence: Letter/Number/Number

	EF	UNC
Prefix U - -, W - - to Y - - followed by serial number	£28	£50
Prefix Z - -	£25	£60

Prefix sequence: Number/Number/Letter

	EF	UNC
Prefix - - A to - - E, - - H to - - K	£15	£35
Prefix - - L	£20	£50

(February 1984)

Predominantly brown. With 0.5mm wide security thread. Printed by intaglio with the reverse by lithography, indicated by small "L" on reverse. 151 x 85mm
Signature: D. H. F. Somerset
Prefix sequence: Letter/Letter/Number/Number

	EF	UNC
Prefix AN - - to AZ - -, BN - - to BZ - -, CN - - to CR - -	£15	£30

(July 1987)

Predominantly brown. With 1mm wide security thread. 151 x 85mm
Signature: D. H. F. Somerset
Prefix sequence: Letter/Letter/Number/Number

	EF	UNC
Prefix CS01 followed by serial number	£30	£70
Prefix CS - - to CZ - -, DN - -	£15	£30

Ten pounds Pictorial series (continued)	*EF*	*UNC*

(March 1988)

Predominantly brown. With windowed security thread. 151 x 85mm
Signature: G. M. Gill
Prefix sequence: Letter/Letter/Number/Number

Prefix DR01 followed by serial number	£20	£50
Prefix DR - - to DZ - -, EN - -, ER - - to EZ - -, HN - -, HR - - to HZ - -, JN - -, JR - -	£15	£25

(November 1991)

Predominantly brown. With windowed security thread. 151 x 85mm
Signature: G. E. A. Kentfield
Prefix sequence: Letter/Letter/Number/Number

Prefix KN01 followed by serial number	£20	£45
Prefix KN - -, KR - -	£14	£35

Collector's packs included notes with first prefix (A01) of the Historical series and last prefix (KR30) of the Pictorial series numbered from 998500 to 999999.

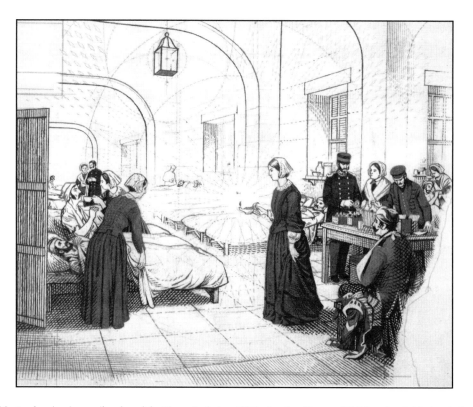

Master drawing in pencil and wash by Harry Eccleston, OBE, showing Florence Nightingale ministering to the sick at Scutari, used on the 1975 £10 note.

Ten pounds (continued)

HISTORICAL SERIES

(April 1992)   *EF*   *UNC*

Predominantly orange. With windowed security thread. 142 x 75mm
Signature: G. E. A. Kentfield
Prefix sequence: Letter/Number/Number
Prefix A01 followed by serial number £12   £25
Prefix A - - to E - -, H - - to L - -, N - -, R - - to Z - - .... —   £20
Prefix M - -, Y - -, Z - - (from special "B" ream) £20   £40
Collector's packs included notes with first prefix (A01) of the Historical series and last
prefix (KR30) of the Pictorial series numbered from 998500 to 999999.

(October 1993)

Predominantly orange but darker printing than previously. 142 x 75mm
Signature: G. E. A. Kentfield
Prefix sequence: Letter/Letter/Number/Number
Prefix DA - - to KK - - followed by serial number .... —   —

(1999)

Predominantly orange. 142 x 75mm
Signature: Merlyn Lowther
Prefix sequence: Letter/Letter/Number/Number
Prefix KL - - to LA - - followed by serial number (KL01 first, LA80 last)   —   £25

TWENTY POUNDS

BLACK AND WHITE SERIES (continued)

(1925–29)	*VF*	*EF*
Signature: C. P. Mahon		
London	£500	£850

(March 1929)

	VF	*EF*
Signature: B. G. Catterns		
London	£400	£850

(1934)

	VF	*EF*
Signature: K. O. Peppiatt		
London	£350	£700

PICTORIAL SERIES

(July 1970)

	EF	*UNC*
Predominantly purple. 160 x 90mm		
Signature: J. S. Fforde		
Prefix sequence: Letter/Number/Number		
PrefixA01 followed by serial number	£140	£250
Prefix A - - (A05 last)..	£60	£180
Prefix M01 (Replacement note)	£150	£300

(1970)

	EF	*UNC*
Predominantly purple. 160 x 90mm		
Signature: J. B. Page		
Prefix sequence: Letter/Number/Number		
Prefix A - -, B - -, C - - (A06 first)	£35	£75
Prefix D - - (D79 last)	£25	£50
Prefix M01 (Replacement note)...	£110	£250
Prefix M - - (Replacement note) (M01 first, M04 last)	£50	£150

Twenty pounds Pictorial series (continued)   EF   UNC

(March 1981)

Predominantly purple. 160 x 90mm
Signature: D. H. F. Somerset
Prefix sequence: Letter/Number/Number
Prefix E - -, H - -, J - - (E01 first, J40 last) £35   £70

(November 1984)

Predominantly purple. Incorporating windowed security thread. 160 x 90mm
Signature: D. H. F. Somerset
Prefix sequence: Number/Number/Letter
Prefix 01A followed by serial number £65   £150
Prefix - - A to - - L (40L last) £35   £75

(March 1988)

Predominantly purple. 160 x 90mm
Signature: G. M. Gill
Prefix sequence: Number/Number/Letter
Prefix 01L followed by serial number £60   £120
Prefix - - L to - - W £35   £65
Prefix - - X (20X last) £80   £160
Collector's packs included notes with last prefix (20X) of the Pictorial series and last prefix (A01) of
the Historical series numbered from 998501 to 999999.

Twenty pounds (continued)   *EF*   *UNC*

HISTORICAL SERIES

(June 1991)

Predominantly purple. With windowed security thread. 149 x 80mm
Signature: G. M. Gill
Prefix sequence: Letter/Number/Number
Prefix A01 followed by serial number £25   £45
Prefix A - - to E - -, H - -, J - -, L - -, R - - .... —   £40
Prefix S - - (S08 last) .... —   —
Collector's packs included notes with first prefix (A01) of the Historical series and last prefix (20X)
of the Pictorial series numbered from 998501 to 999999.

(early 1993)

Predominantly purple. 149 x 80mm
Signature: G. E. A. Kentfield
Prefix sequence: Letter/Number/Number
Prefix E01 followed by serial number .... —   £80
Prefix E - -, H - - to L - -, N - -, R - - to U - -, W - - .... —   £40
Prefix W35 (last) .... —   £90
Prefix A71 to A99, B71 to B89, C71 to C - -, Z01 to Z90 (from special "B" Ream)   £80

(September 1993)

Predominantly purple. 149 x 80mm
Signature: G. E. A. Kentfield
Prefix sequence: Letter/Number/Number
Prefix X01 followed by serial number .... —   £45
Prefix X - -, Y - - (Y70 last) .... —   £35
Prefix sequence: Letter/Letter/Number/Number
Prefix AA01 followed by serial number .... —   £180
Prefix AA - - to CL - - .... —   —

(January 1999)

Predominantly purple. 149 x 80mm
Signature: Merlyn Lowther
Prefix sequence: Letter/Letter/Number/Number
Prefix DA - - to - - - - followed by serial number (DA01 first) .... —   £45

Twenty pounds Historical series (continued)   EF   UNC

(June 1999) *Revised design. Reverse depicting Sir Edward Elgar*

Predominantly purple. 149 x 80mm
Signature: Merlyn Lowther
Prefix sequence: Letter/Letter/Number/Number
Prefix AA01 followed by serial number ....   —   £30

Old Mercers' Hall in the City of London, where the Bank of England was first established.

FIFTY POUNDS

BLACK AND WHITE SERIES continued

	VF	EF
(1925–29)		
Signature: C. P. Mahon		
London	£500	£850
(March 1929)		
Signature: B. G. Catterns		
London	£400	£750
(1934)		
Signature: K. O. Peppiatt		
London	£300	£650

Fifty pounds (continued)   EF   UNC

PICTORIAL SERIES

	EF	UNC

(March 1981)

Multicoloured. 169 x 95mm
Signature: D. H. F. Somerset
Prefix sequence: Letter/Number/Number

	EF	UNC
PrefixA01 followed by serial number	£85	£150
Prefix A - -, B - -	—	£100
Prefix B90	£85	£150

(July 1988)

Multicoloured. With windowed security thread. 169 x 95mm
Signature: G. M. Gill
Prefix sequence: Letter/Number/Number

	EF	UNC
Prefix C01 followed by serial number	£110	£230
Prefix C - -to E - -	£80	£120
Prefix D90	£85	£180
Prefix D91 to D95, E16 to E30 (Replacement notes)	£100	£200

(November 1991)

Multicoloured. 169 x 95mm
Signature: G. E. A. Kentfield
Prefix sequence: Letter/Number/Number

	EF	UNC
Prefix E01 followed by serial number	—	£125
Prefix E - -	—	£100
Prefix E30 (last)	—	£140

Collector's packs included notes with last prefix (E30) of the Pictorial series and first prefix (A01) of the Historical series numbered from 998500 to 999999.

Fifty pounds (continued)   *EF*   *UNC*

HISTORICAL SERIES

(April 1994)

Predominantly red. 169 x 95mm
Signature: G. E. A. Kentfield
Prefix sequence: Letter/Number/Number
Prefix A01 followed by serial number ....   —   £100
Prefix A - - ....   —   £95
Collector's packs included notes with first prefix (A01) of the Historical series and last prefix (E30)
of the Pictorial series numbered from 998500 to 999999.

(January 1999)

Predominantly red. 169 x 95mm
Signature: Merlyn Lowther
Prefix sequence: Letter/Number/Number
Prefix J01 followed by serial number ....   —   £120

The banknotes of Scotland

The first Scottish notes appeared in 1695 in the year of the foundation of the Bank of Scotland and contemporary with the earliest notes of the Bank of England. They were released in values from £5 to £100 sterling; when pound notes appeared in 1704 they were denominated £12 Scots, reflecting the prevailing exchange rate. The Bank's monopoly expired in 1721 and within six years it was faced with a rival with the title of the Royal Bank of Scotland, although the general public referred to them simply as the Old and New Banks.

Both banks originated from a need to put banking on a proper footing and supply paper money for the convenience of the mercantile classes. The third bank, however, appeared in 1746 with the primary objective of stimulating the linen industry, and this was reflected in its name, the British Linen Company which did not change its title to the British Linen Bank until 1906. In the second half of the 18th century smaller banks appeared in various parts of the country, usually confined to a specific locality. Although these banks did much to foster trade and industry in their own areas, the spectacular crash of Douglas Heron & Company in 1772 bankrupted many of the leading families in the south-west of Scotland. Many of the smaller banks, confined to a single town, were fairly ephemeral, remembered by their elusive notes which are now much sought after by collectors of local history as well as notaphilists.

Early in the 19th century, however, there emerged a number of joint-stock banks which were destined to play a major role in the economic development of Scotland. These included the Caledonian Banking Company (1838–1907), the Central Bank (1834–68), the City of Glasgow Bank (1839–79), the Clydesdale Bank (1838), the Commercial Bank (1810–1959), the Eastern Bank (1838–63), the National Bank (1825–1959), the North of Scotland Bank (1836–1950), the Town & County Bank (1825–1908), the Union Bank (1843–1955) and the Western Bank (1832–57). Although the Bank Charter Act of 1844 severely restricted the note-issuing activities of the English provincial banks, the comparable legislation for Scotland a year later enabled the Scottish banks to continue to issue their own notes, although the act banned the foundation of any new note-issuing banks after that date.

Although banking in Scotland was on a sounder footing than in England, the failure of the West of Scotland Bank in 1857 and the City of Glasgow Bank in 1878 both had severe repercussions on the economy of the west of Scotland. The worst effects, so far as the general public possessing notes of these banks was concerned, were mitigated by the undertaking of the National Bank to redeem the notes of the West of Scotland, and by all the other banks acting in concert to redeem the City of Glasgow notes.

As a result of mergers and amalgamations the number of note-issuing banks gradually fell, although by the beginning of the 20th century there were still ten in existence. The Caledonian was absorbed by the Bank of Scotland in 1907 and the Town & County merged with the North of Scotland Bank the following year. In the period after World War II there were further amalgamations. For example, in 1959 the Commercial Bank joined forces with the National Bank to form the National Commercial Bank of Scotland which, in turn, combined with the Royal Bank of Scotland which now acquired the suffix "Limited" inscribed on notes since that date. In the same year the British Linen Bank (acquired by Barclays in 1919) was sold to the Bank of Scotland and the merger was completed the following year.

Of the 19th century joint-stock banks, only the Clydesdale has survived, although it, too, has undergone enormous changes. It was formed in 1838 by the union of the Greenock Union Bank, the Edinburgh & Glasgow Bank, the Eastern Bank and the Dundee Commercial Bank. In 1919 it was acquired by the Midland Bank which four years later also took over the North of Scotland Bank. These banks continued to operate separately until 1950 when they merged to form the Clydesdale & North of Scotland Bank which reverted to the shorter title of the Clydesdale Bank in 1963.

Today, therefore, Scotland enjoys the colourful variety of notes produced by three banks, a far cry from the relatively plain black and white notes of the 18th and early 19th centuries. Although many of the earlier notes were engraved and printed by local firms such as Kirkwood, Lizars and Johnston, later notes were produced by the great English security printers, from Perkins Bacon to De La Rue. Prior to the late 1960s there was no uniformity regarding size or colours but since then both have been brought into line with the notes of the Bank of England. In 1975 James Douglas estimated the total circulation of the three Scottish banks in excess of £250 million, or about 7 per cent of the total for the British Isles. The Royal Bank is now the only Scottish bank to continue issuing pound notes and all three have notes up to £100. Moreover, they have shown a penchant for commemorative notes in recent years, notably the Royal Bank's pounds honouring Alexander Graham Bell, Robert Louis Stevenson and the advent of the Scottish Parliament, and the Clydesdale's £20 notes for the Commonwealth Heads of Government Meeting (1997) and Glasgow and UK City of Architecture and Design (1999), not to mention the series of four £5 notes of 1996 marking the bicentenary of Robert Burns by including verses from his poems.

In this edition of the BANKNOTE YEARBOOK for the sake of simplicity it has been decided to include only the notes of the current issuing banks and their constituent companies.

BANK OF SCOTLAND

ONE POUND

1889–1929 ISSUE

VF   EF

Yellow-brown and grey. 165 x 120mm
Signatures:
J. F. Stormonth Darling (Nov. 16, 1889–Feb. 21, 1893) £250   £550
D. McNeill (Feb. 18, 1894–Dec. 19, 1910) £180   £400
P. MacDonald (Jan. 3, 1911–Nov. 24, 1920) £150   £205
A. Rose (Dec. 8, 1920–Nov. 16, 1927) £110   £180

1929–35 ISSUE

Yellow-brown and grey. 152 x 84mm
Signatures:
(Lord) Elphinstone and G. J. Scott £40   £90

1935–43 ISSUE

Yellow-brown and grey. 152 x 84mm
Signatures:
(Lord) Elphinstone and A. W. M. Beveridge £30   £50
(Lord) Elphinstone and J. Macfarlane £20   £40
(Lord) Elphinstone and J. B. Crawford £15   £35

	VF	EF

1945 ISSUE

Yellow and grey. 152 x 84mm
Signatures:
(Lord) Elphinstone and J. B. Crawford (Jan. 4–Feb. 6, 1945) £50   £100
(Lord) Elphinstone and J. B. Crawford (Feb. 6, 1945–Nov. 19, 1952) £12   £30
L(Lord) Elphinstone and (Sir) Wm. Watson (Sept. 4, Oct. 16, Nov. 9, 1953)   £10   £30

1955–60 ISSUE

Light brown and blue. 152 x 84mm
Signatures:
(Lord) Elphinstone and (Sir) Wm. Watson (March 1, 2, 3, 4, 1955) £8   £30
(Sir) J. Craig and (Sir) Wm. Watson (Sept. 1, 1955–Sept 14, 1956) £8   £20
(Lord) Bilsland and (Sir) Wm. Watson (Aug. 30, 1957–Nov. 30, 1960) £5   £15

1961 ISSUE

Light brown and blue. 150 x 72mm
Signatures:
(Lord) Bilsland and (Sir) Wm. Watson
    With printer's imprint "LD" (May 10, 1961–Feb. 13 1964) £5   £15
    With printer's imprint "LTD" (May 4, 1965, May 11, 1965) £4   £12

VF   EF

1966 ISSUE

Light brown and blue. 150 x 72mm
Signatures:
(Lord) Polwarth and J. Letham
    Without electronic sorting marks on reverse (June 1, 1966) £5   £10
    With electronic sorting marks on reverse (March 3, 1967).............. £6   £12

1968–69 ISSUE

Ochre. 135 x 67mm
Signatures:
(Lord) Polwarth and J. Letham
    "EDINBURGH" 19mm long (July 17, 1968) £8   £15
    "EDINBURGH" 24mm long (Aug. 18, 1969) £7   £14

1970–74 ISSUE

Green. 135 x 67mm
Signatures:
(Lord) Polwarth and T. W. Walker (Aug. 10, 1970, Aug. 31, 1971) £5   £12
(Lord) Clydesmuir and T. W. Walker (Nov. 1, 1972, Aug. 30, 1973) £5   £10
(Lord) Clydesmuir and A. M. Russell (Oct. 28, 1974–Oct. 3, 1978)............ £3   £8
(Lord) Clydesmuir and D. B. Pattullo (October 15, 1979, Nov. 4, 1980) £2   £7
(Sir) T. N. Risk and D. B. Pattullo (with sorting marks) (July 30, 1981)....... £3   £7
(Sir) T. N. Risk and D. B. Pattullo (without sorting marks) (Oct. 7, 1983,
Nov. 9, 1984, Dec. 12, 1985, Nov. 18, 1986) £2   £6
(Sir) T. N. Risk and L. P. Burt (Aug. 19, 1988) £2   £4

	VF	*EF*

FIVE POUNDS

1889–1930 ISSUE

Yellow-brown and grey. 220 x 135mm
Signatures:

J. F. Stormonth Darling (May 24, 1889–Feb. 20, 1893)	£425	£850
D. McNeill (May 5, 1894–Oct. 17 1911)	£350	£500
P. MacDonald (Sep. 18, 1912–Oct. 4, 1916)	£200	£325
A. Rose (Dec. 8, 1920–Oct. 11, 1932)	£140	£240

1933–44 ISSUE

Yellow-brown and grey. 220 x 135mm
Signatures:

(Lord) Elphinstone and G. J. Scott (Feb. 10–Mar. 25, 1933)	£90	£150

Yellow-brown and grey. 220 x 135mm
Signatures:

(Lord) Elphinstone and A. W. M. Beveridge	£80	£125
(Lord) Elphinstone and J. Macfarlane	£70	£100
(Lord) Elphinstone and J. B. Crawford	£55	£85

VF   *EF*

1945 ISSUE

Grey and brown. 180 x 102mm
Signatures:
(Lord) Elphinstone and J. B. Crawford
Dark brown reverse (Jan. 3, Jan. 15, Feb. 1, March 2, 1945) £55   £120
Light brown reverse (March 16, 1945–June 10, 1948) £40   £85

1948 ISSUE

Grey and brown. 180 x 102mm
Signatures:
(Lord) Elphinstone and J. B. Crawford (Nov. 16, 1948–Nov. 21, 1952) £30   £65
(Lord) Elphinstone and (Sir) Wm. Watson (Dec. 10, 1952–Dec. 4, 1953) £35   £70

1955 ISSUE

Light brown and blue. 180 x 102mm
Signatures:
(Lord) Elphinstone and (Sir) Wm. Watson £35   £110
(Sir) J. Craig and (Sir) Wm. Watson £40   £130

1956–60 ISSUE

Light brown and blue. 180 x 102mm
Signatures:
(Sir) J. Craig and (Sir) Wm. Watson £22   £50
(Lord) Bilsland and (Sir) Wm. Watson £18   £35

	VF	UNC

1961 ISSUE (Hollow Figs of Value)

Light brown and blue. 140 x 84mm
Signatures:
(Lord) Bilsland and (Sir) Wm. Watson £15 £45

1961–66 ISSUE (Solid Figs of Value)

Light brown and blue. 140 x 84mm
Signatures:
(Lord) Bilsland and (Sir) Wm. Watson.. £12 £40
(Lord) Polwarth and (Sir) Wm. Watson £20 £45
(Lord) Polwarth and J. Letham
   Without electronic sorting marks on reverse (Feb. 1–2, 1967) £20 £40
   With electronic sorting marks on reverse (Nov. 11, 1967) £25 £50

1968–69 ISSUE

Green. 146 x 78mm
Signatures:
(Lord) Polwarth and J. Letham
"EDINBURGH" 19mm long (Nov. 1, 1968) £35 £75
"EDINBURGH" 24mm long (Dec. 8, 1969) £35 £80

1970–88 ISSUE

Blue. 146 x 78mm
Signatures:
(Lord) Polwarth and T. W. Walker (Aug. 10, 1970, Sep. 2, 1971) £20 £40
(Lord) Clydesmuir and T. W. Walker (Dec. 4, 1972, Sep. 5, 1973) £15 £35
(Lord) Clydesmuir and A. M. Russell (Nov. 4, 1974, Dec. 1, 1975, Nov. 21, 1977,
Oct. 19, 1978) £15 £35
(Lord) Clydesmuir and D. B. Pattullo (Oct. 28, 1979, Nov. 28, 1980) £15 £30
(Sir) T. N. Risk and D. B. Pattullo (sorting marks) (Jul. 27, 1981, Jun. 25, 1982)£12 £25
(Sir) T. N. Risk and D. B. Pattullo (no sorting marks) (Oct. 13, 1983, Feb. 1988) £8 £20

Five pounds (continued)	*VF*	*UNC*

1990–92 ISSUE (as above but reduced size)

Blue. 135 x 70mm
Signatures:

(Sir) T. N. Risk and P. Burt	—	£15
D. B. Pattullo and P. Burt	—	£15

1995 ISSUE

Dark blue and purple. 135 x 70mm
Signatures:

D. B. Pattullo and P. Burt	—	£12
Bruce Pattullo and G. Masterton	—	£10
A. Grant and G. Masterton	—	£10

	VF	*EF*

TEN POUNDS

1889–1929 ISSUE

Yellow-brown and grey. 206 x 130mm
Signatures:

J. F. Stormonth Darling (Dec. 23, 1890)	£450	£750
D. McNeill (Oct. 16, 1894–Sep. 30, 1909)	£400	£700
P. MacDonald (Nov. 20, 1912–Nov. 5, 1919)	£350	£600
A. Rose (Aug. 15, 1921–Mar. 9, 1929)	£300	£500

1935 ISSUE (Royal Arms)

Yellow-brown and grey. 206 x 130mm
Signatures:

(Lord) Elphinstone and A. W. M. Beveridge	£190	£130

1938–42 ISSUE

Yellow-brown and grey. 206 x 130mm
Signatures:

(Lord) Elphinstone and A. W. M. Beveridge	£180	£270
(Lord) Elphinstone and J. B. Crawford	£140	£230

1963 ISSUE

Yellow-brown and blue. 206 x 130mm
Signatures:

(Lord) EBilsland and (Sir) Wm. Watson	£120	£190

Ten pounds (continued)   *EF*   *UNC*

1970–90 ISSUE

Brown. 158 x 89mm
Signatures:
(Lord) Clydesmuir and A. M. Russell £30   £60
(Lord) Clydesmuir and D. B. Pattullo £35   £70
(Sir) T. N. Risk and D. B. Pattullo .... —   £35
(Sir) T. N. Risk and P. Burt .... —   £30

1992–94 ISSUE (as above but reduced size)

Brown. 142 x 75mm
Signatures:
D. B. Pattullo and P. Burt .... —   £25

1995 ISSUE

Brown and green. 135 x 70mm
Signatures:
D. B. Pattullo and P. Burt .... —   £20
Bruce Pattullo and G. Masterton .... —   £18
A. Grant and G. Masterton .... —   £15

VF   EF

TWENTY POUNDS

1890–1932 ISSUE

Yellow-brown and grey with red panels. 206 x 130mm
Signatures:

	VF	EF
J. F. Stormonth Darling (July 9, 1890–Jan. 30, 1893)	£600	£1200
D. McNeill (May 26, 1894–Sep. 2, 1910)	£450	£900
P. MacDonald (Oct. 26, 1911–Dec. 29, 1920)	£400	£750
A. Rose (Oct. 1921–June 21, 1932)	£350	£700

1932–35 ISSUE

Yellow-brown and grey. 206 x 130mm
Signatures:

	VF	EF
(Lord) Elphinstone and G. J. Scott	£190	£400
(Lord) Elphinstone and A. W. M. Beveridge	£150	£300

1936–63 ISSUE

VF   EF

Yellow-brown and grey (from 1956 yellow-brown and blue). 206 x 130mm
Signatures:

	VF	EF
(Lord) Elphinstone and A. W. M. Beveridge	£100	£200
(Lord) Elphinstone and J. Macfarlane	£80	£165
(Lord) Elphinstone and J. B. Crawford	£70	£140
(Lord) Elphinstone and (Sir) Wm. Watson	£80	£100
(Sir) J. Craig and (Sir) Wm. Watson	£70	£135

1969 ISSUE

Yellow-brown and grey. 206 x 130mm. With security thread
Signatures:

	VF	EF
(Lord) Polwarth and J. Letham (emergency printing)	£75	£160

Twenty pounds (continued)   *EF*   *UNC*

1970–87 ISSUE

Purple. 182 x 99mm
Signatures:
(Lord) Polwarth and T. W. Walker £110   £200
(Lord) Clydesmuir and T. W. Walker £110   £200
(Lord) Clydesmuir and A. M. Russell £70   £150
(Lord) Clydesmuir and D. B. Pattullo £65   £140
(Sir) T. N. Risk and D. B. Pattullo £40   £100

1991–93 ISSUE (as above but reduced size)

Purple. 148 x 81mm
Signatures:
D. B. Pattullo and P. Burt .... —   £40

1995 ISSUE

Violet and brown. 148 x 81mm
Signatures:
D. B. Pattullo and P. Burt .... —   £35
Bruce Pattullo and G. Masterton .... —   £30
A. Grant and G. Masterton .... —   £25

EF   UNC

FIFTY POUNDS

1995 ISSUE

Green and brown. 148 x 81mm
Signatures:
D. B. Pattullo and P. Burt £50   £75

ONE HUNDRED POUNDS

VF   EF

1889–1930 ISSUE

Yellow-brown and grey with red panels. 206 x 130mm
Signatures:
J. F. Stormonth Darling (Aug. 27, 1889–Feb. 10, 1893) £1000   £2000
D. McNeill (July 12, 1894–Dec. 9, 1910) £500   £1000
P. MacDonald (Dec. 11, 1911–Apr. 17, 1919) £475   £900
A. Rose (July 7, 1920–June 8, 1930) £450   £750

1929–35 ISSUE

Yellow-brown and grey. 206 x 130mm
Signatures:
(Lord) Elphinstone and G. J. Scott £480   £900
(Lord) Elphinstone and A. W. M. Beveridge £430   £850

1937–62 ISSUE

Yellow-brown and grey (from 1956 yellow-brown and blue). 206 x 130mm
Signatures:
(Lord) Elphinstone and A. W. M. Beveridge £350   £700
(Lord) Elphinstone and J. Macfarlane £300   £600
(Lord) Elphinstone and J. B. Crawford £230   £480
(Lord) Bilsland and (Sir) Wm. Watson £180   £400

One hundred pounds (continued)   *EF*   *UNC*

1971–94 ISSUE

Red. 182 x 99mm
Signatures:

	EF	UNC
(Lord) Polwarth and T.W. Walker	£250	£400
(Lord) Clydesmuir and T. W. Walker	£180	£350
(Lord) Clydesmuir and A. M. Russell	£150	£300
(Lord) clydesmuir and D. B. Pattullo	£140	£280
Sir Thomas Risk and D. B. Pattullo	—	£200
Sir Thomas Risk and P. Burt	—	£250
D. B. Pattullo and P. Burt	—	£195

1995 ISSUE

Violet, red and orange. 148 x 81mm
Signatures:

	EF	UNC
D. B. Pattullo and P. Burt	—	£160
Bruce Pattullo and Gavin Masterton	—	£145

THE CLYDESDALE BANK LTD. (1882–1950)

ONE POUND

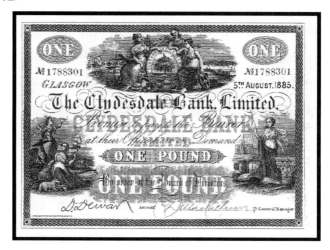

	VF	EF

1882 ISSUE

Black and red. 165 x 120mm
Signatures: D. Dewar (printed) and proxy handwritten signature for General Manager
Without prefix letter to serial number (1882–1912) £250 £400
With prefix letter to serial number (1913–21) £175 £325

1922 ISSUE

Blue and red. 165 x 120mm
Signatures:
A. Swanson and D. Dewar (1922) £300 £450
A. Swanson and R. Young (1923–26) £250 £375

The Clydesdale Bank Ltd. One pound (continued)	*VF*	*EF*

1927 ISSUE

Blue and red. 152 x 85mm
Signatures:

A. Swanson and R. Young (1927–31)	£35	£75
A. Mitchell and R. Young (1932–45)	£25	£55
A. Mitchell and J. W. Pairman (May 1946)	£35	£75
J. J. Campbell and J. W. Pairman (Nov. 1946–1947)	£25	£50
J. J. Campbell and R. R. Houston (1948–49)	£25	£50

FIVE POUNDS

1882 ISSUE

Black and red. 225 x 125mm
Signatures: D. Dewar (printed) and proxy handwritten signature for General Manager

1882–1921	£440	£750

1922–48 ISSUE

Blue and red. 225 x 125mm
Signatures:

A. Swanson and J. D. Dewar (1922)	£170	£300
A. Swanson and R. Young (1923–31)	£130	£250
A. Mitchell and R. Young (1932–45)	£100	£200
J. J. Campbell and J. W. Pairman (1946)	£60	£120
J. J. Campbell and J. W. Pairman (1948)	£95	£180
J. J. Campbell and R. R. Houston (1949)	£95	£180

The Clydesdale Bank Ltd. (continued)   *VF*   *EF*

TWENTY POUNDS

1882 ISSUE

Black and red. 165 x 120mm
Signatures: D. Dewar (printed) and proxy handwritten signature for General Manager
1882–1920 .... £400   £750

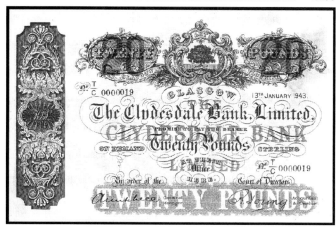

1922–47 ISSUE

Blue and red. 225 x 125mm
Signatures:
A. Swanson and J. D. Dewar (1922–23) £200   £390
A. Swanson and R. Young (1923–31) £200   £370
A. Mitchell and R. Young (1932–44) £130   £350
J. J. Campbell and J. W. Pairman (1947) £75   £180

ONE HUNDRED POUNDS

1922–47 ISSUE

Blue and red. 225 x 125mm
Signatures:
A. Swanson and J. D. Dewar (1922) .... —   —
A. Swanson and R. Young (1925–31) .... —   —
A. Mitchell and R. Young (1935–43) £500   £750
J. J. Campbell and J. W. Pairman (1947) £550   £800

CLYDESDALE AND NORTH OF SCOTLAND BANK LIMITED (1950–63)

ONE POUND

1950–51 ISSUE	VF	EF
Blue-gey and orange. 152 x 85mm		
Signatures:		
J. J. Campbell (1950–56)	£12	£30
R. D. Fairbairn (1958–60)	£10	£25

1961 ISSUE

Green and orange. 152 x 72mm
Signature: R. D. Fairbairn (1961–63) £8   £20

FIVE POUNDS

1950–51 ISSUE

Purple, red and green. 179 x 98mm
Signatures:
J. J. Campbell (1951–56) £20   £40
R. D. Fairbairn (1960) £20   £40

The Clydesdale Bank Ltd. Five pounds (continued)   *VF*   *EF*

1961 ISSUE

Blue, green, red and orange. 141 x 84mm
Signature: R. D. Fairbairn (1961–63) £15   £30

TWENTY POUNDS

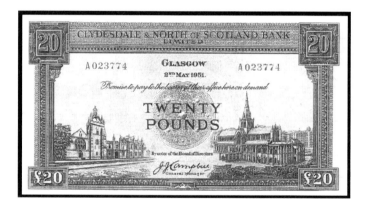

1950–51 ISSUE

Green, brown and yellow. 179 x 98mm
Signatures:
J. J. Campbell (1951–58) £40   £90
R. D. Fairbairn (1960–62) £40   £90

The Clydesdale Bank Ltd. (continued)   EF   UNC

ONE HUNDRED POUNDS

1951 ISSUE £100

Blue-green and yellow. 179 x 98mm
Signatures:
J. J. Campbell (1951) £500   £900
R. D. Fairbairn (1960) £450   £900

CLYDESDALE BANK LTD (1963–81)

ONE POUND

	EF	UNC

1963–64 ISSUE

Green, orange and red. 152 x 72mm
Signatures:

	EF	UNC
R. D. Fairbairn (1963–69)	£15	£25

1971-81 ISSUE

Green and multicolour. 134.5 x 67mm
Signatures:

	EF	UNC
R. D. Fairbairn (1971)	£10	£20
A. R. Macmillan (1972–73)	£8	£18
A. R. Macmillan (1974–81)	£5	£12

Clydesdale Bank Ltd. (continued)   *EF*   *UNC*

FIVE POUNDS

1963–64 ISSUE

Green, orange and red. 152 x 72mm
Signatures:
R. D. Fairbairn (1963–69) £25   £50

1971–81 ISSUE

Green and multicolour. 146 x 78mm
Signatures:
R. D. Fairbairn (1971) £30   £60
A. R. Macmillan (1972–73) £25   £50
A. R. Macmillan (1974–80) £20   £45

TEN POUNDS

1963–64 ISSUE

Brown, green and red. 152 x 94mm
Signatures:
R. D. Fairbairn (1964–67) £100   £220

1971–81 ISSUE

Brown and multicolour. 152 x 85mm
Signatures:
A. R. Macmillan (1972–73) £40   £90
A. R. Macmillan (1974–81) £35   £70

Clydesdale Bank Ltd. (continued)   *EF*   *UNC*

TWENTY POUNDS

1963–64 ISSUE

Red and green. 162 x 93mm
Signatures:
R. D. Fairbairn (1964–67) £80   £160

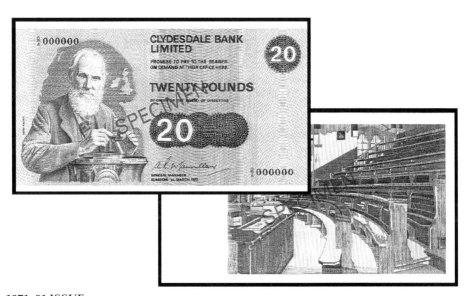

1971–81 ISSUE

Purple and multicolour. 161 x 91mm
Signatures:
A. R. Macmillan (1972) £90   £180
A. R. Macmillan (1976, 1981) £75   £150

Clydesdale Bank Ltd. (continued)   *EF*   *UNC*

FIFTY POUNDS

1971–81 ISSUE

Olive and multicolour. 161 x 91mm
Signature:
A. R. Macmillan (1981) £80   £120

ONE HUNDRED POUNDS

1963–64 ISSUE

Green, orange and red. 162 x 93mm
Signatures:
R. D. Fairbairn (1965–68) £350   £750

1971–81 ISSUE

Red and multicolour. 152 x 85mm
Signatures:
A. R. Macmillan (1972) £220   £400
A. R. Macmillan (1976) £180   £380

CLYDESDALE BANK PLC (from 1981)

ONE POUND

1982–89 ISSUE

Green and multicolour. 134.5 x 67mm	*EF*	*UNC*
Signatures:		
A. R. Macmillan (1982)	£5	£10
A. R. Cole Hamilton (1983–85)	£5	£10
A. R. Cole Hamilton (1988)	£4	£8

FIVE POUNDS

1982–89 ISSUE

Green and multicolour. 146 x 78mm		
Signatures:		
A. R. Macmillan (1982)	£25	£45
A. R. Cole Hamilton (1983–85)	£15	£35
A. R. Cole Hamilton (1986–89)	£15	£30

Clydesdale Bank plc. Five pounds (continued)   *EF*   *UNC*

1989–96 ISSUE

Black and multicolour. 135 x 70mm
Signatures:
A. R. Cole Hamilton (1990) £10   £15
F. Cicutto (1994) £8   £12
F. Goodwin (1996-97) £8   £12

1996 COMMEMORATIVE ISSUE

Black and multicolour. 135 x 70mm (one million of each printed)
Signature:
F. Goodwin £8   £15
Four variants, each with a different quote from Robert Burns
Set of 4

Clydesdale Bank plc. (continued) 　　　　　　　　　　　　　　　　　　　*EF*　　　　*UNC*

TEN POUNDS

1982–89 ISSUE

Brown, purple and multicolour. 152 x 85mm
Signatures:
A. R. Macmillan (1982) .... £75　　　£140
A. R. Cole Hamilton (1983–86) .... £60　　　£120
A. R. Cole Hamilton (1987) .... £60　　　£110

1988 ISSUE

Brown and multicolour. 152 x 85mm
Signatures:
A. R. Cole Hamilton (1988–90) .... £25　　　£45

1992–96 ISSUE

Brown and multicolour. As above but reduced size 142 x 75mm
Signatures:
A. R. Cole Hamilton (1992) .... £15　　　£30
Charles Love (1993) .... £15　　　£30
F. Goodwin (1996–97) .... £14　　　£25

Clydesdale Bank plc. Ten pounds (continued)   *EF*   *UNC*

1997–2000 ISSUE

Brown and multicolour. 142 x 75mm
Signatures:

	EF	UNC
F. Goodwin (1997)	£12	£18
F. Wright (1998–2000)	—	£15
1997 issue specially encapsulated in acrylic plastic case for presentation	—	£80
Millennium MM prefix	—	£20

TWENTY POUNDS

1982–89 ISSUE

Brown, purple and multicolour. 161 x 91mm
Signatures:

	EF	UNC
A. R. Macmillan (1982)	£75	£150
A. R. Cole Hamilton (1983–85)	£75	£140
A. R. Cole Hamilton (1987, 1990)	£60	£120

1989–96 ISSUE

Purple and multicolour. 150 x 80mm
Signatures:

	EF	UNC
A. R. Cole Hamilton (1990–92)	—	£45
Charles Love (1993)	—	£45
F. Cicutto (1994)	—	£45
F. Goodwin (1996)	—	£40
F. Goodwin (1997)	—	£40
F. Wright (1999–)	—	£35

Clydesdale Bank plc. Twenty pounds (continued)   *EF*   *UNC*

1997 COMMEMORATIVE ISSUE

Commonwealth Heads of Government meeting in Edinburgh

Purple, orange and multicolour. 150 x 80mm
Signature:
F. Goodwin £45

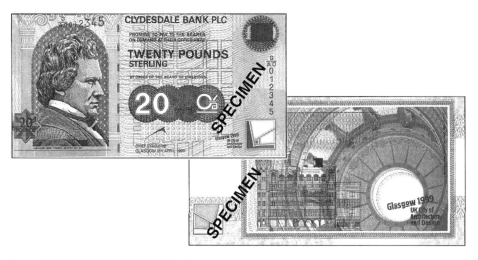

1999 COMMEMORATIVE ISSUE

Glasgow, Architecture and Design

Purple, orange and multicolour. 150 x 80mm
Signature:
F. Wright £38

2000 COMMEMORATIVE ISSUE

Millennium MM prefix

Purple, orange and multicolour. 150 x 80mm
Signature:
F. Wright £38

Clydesdale Bank plc. (continued)   *EF*   *UNC*

FIFTY POUNDS

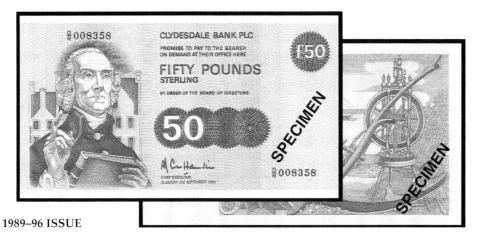

1989–96 ISSUE

Olive green and multicolour. 171 x 96mm
Signatures:
A. R. Cole Hamilton (1989–92) ....   —   £100

1996 ISSUE

Green, brown and multicolour. 156 x 85mm
Signatures:
F. Goodwin ....   —   £75

2001 ISSUE (350th Anniversary of Glasgow University, special GU prefix)

Green, brown and multicolour. 156 x 85mm
Signatures:
S. Grimshaw ....   —   £70

Clydesdale Bank plc. (continued)   EF   UNC

ONE HUNDRED POUNDS

1982–89 ISSUE

Red and multicolour. 161 x 90mm
Signatures:
A. R. Cole Hamilton £150   £250

1996 ISSUE

Purple, red and multicolour. 163 x 90mm
Signatures:
F. Goodwin .... —   £175

2001 ISSUE (350th Anniversary of Glasgow University, special GU prefix)

Purple, red and multicolour. 163 x 90mm
Signatures:
S. Grimshaw .... —   £150

THE ROYAL BANK OF SCOTLAND

ONE POUND

	VF	EF

1887 ISSUE

Blue and red on yellow background. 174 x 128mm
Signatures:

	VF	EF
W. Templeton (1887–Jan. 1908)	£250	£450
D. S. Lunan (May 1908–Mar. 1920)	£100	£150
D. Speed (May 1920–May. 1926)	£75	£150

1927 ISSUE

Blue on pale yellow background. 152 x 84mm
Signatures:

	VF	EF
D. Speed (1927–36)	£55	£100

1937 ISSUE

Blue on yellow background. 152 x 84mm
Signatures:

	VF	EF
D. Speed (1937–42)	£75	£100
T. Brown (1943–51)	£45	£75
J. D. C. Dick (1951–55)	£35	£45

The Royal Bank of Scotland. One pound (continued)   EF   UNC

1955 ISSUE

Blue on deep yellow background. 152 x 84mm
Signatures:
W. R. Ballantyne (1955–64) £75   £100

1964 ISSUE

Blue on deep yellow background. 150 x 71mm
Signatures:
W. R. Ballantyne (1964–65) £5   £15
A. P. Robertson (1965–67) £5   £15

1967 ISSUE

Green and multicolour. 135 x 67mm
Signatures:
A. P. Robertson £8   £18

The Royal Bank of Scotland. One pound (continued)   EF   UNC

FIVE POUNDS

1887 ISSUE

Blue and red on yellow background. 206 x 130mm
Signatures:

	EF	UNC
Accountant and Cashier (1875–1918)	£250	£750
D. Speed (1923–Jan. 1942)	£100	£250
Cashier, General Manager and Chief Accountant (July 1942– 50)	£45	£85

1953 ISSUE

Blue and red on yellow background. 182 x 99mm
Signatures:

	EF	UNC
I. M. Thomson and J. D. C. Dick (1952–53)	£75	£125
W. A. Watt, W. R. Ballantyne and J. D. C. Dick (1953–54)	£55	£100
W. R. Ballantyne and A. G. Campbell (1955–63)	£45	£65

1964 ISSUE

Blue, brown and yellow. 140 x 85mm
Signatures:

	EF	UNC
W. R. Ballantyne and A. G. Campbell (1964)	£25	£55
A. P. Robertson and A. G. Campbell (1965)	£25	£55

1967 ISSUE

Blue and multicolour. 146 x 78mm
Signatures:

	EF	UNC
A. P. Robertson and A. G. Campbell	£25	£55

TEN POUNDS

1887 ISSUE

Blue and red on yellow background. 206 x 130mm
Signatures:

	VF	EF
On behalf of Accountant and Cashier (1877–1917)	£450	£850
On behalf of Accountant and Cashier (1918–40)	£200	£350
On behalf of Accountant and Cashier (1940–69)	£150	£250

TWENTY POUNDS

1887 ISSUE

Blue and red on yellow background. 206 x 130mm
Signatures:

	VF	EF
On behalf of Accountant and Cashier (1877–1912)	£300	£450
On behalf of Accountant and Cashier (1912–47)	£125	£200
On behalf of Accountant and Cashier (1947–69)	£65	£100

ONE HUNDRED POUNDS

1887 ISSUE

Blue and red on yellow background. 206 x 130mm
Signatures:

	VF	EF
On behalf of Accountant and Cashier (1877–1912)	£450	£850
On behalf of Accountant and Cashier (1912–49)	£250	£450
I. M. Thomson and T. Brown (1949)	£250	£450
W. R. Ballantyne and A. G. Campbell (1960)	£200	£350
A. P. Robertson and A. G. Campbell (1966)	£200	£350

THE ROYAL BANK OF SCOTLAND LTD

ONE POUND

1969 ISSUE	*EF*	*UNC*

Green on multicolour. 135 x 67mm
Signatures:

A. P. Robertson and J. B. Burke (1969)	£10	£14
J. B. Burke (1970)	£7	£14

1972 ISSUE

Dark green on multicolour. 135 x 67mm
Signature:

J. B. Burke	£2	£6

The Royal Bank of Scotland Ltd. (continued)   *EF*   *UNC*

FIVE POUNDS

1969, 1970 ISSUES

Blue on multicolour. 146 x 78mm
Signatures:
A. P. Robertson and J. B. Burke (1969) £32   £50
J. B. Burke (1970) £32   £50

1972 ISSUE

Blue on multicolour. 146 x 78mm
Signature:
J. B. Burke £26   £50

TEN POUNDS

1969 ISSUE

Brown on multicolour. 158 x 89mm
Signatures:
A. P. Robertson and J. B. Burke £80   £100

The Royal Bank of Scotland Ltd. Ten pounds (continued)   EF   UNC

1972 ISSUE

Brown on multicolour. 158 x 89mm
Signature:
J. B. Burke £35   £95

TWENTY POUNDS

1969 ISSUE

Purple on multicolour. 182 x 99mm
Signatures:
A. P. Robertson and J. B. Burke £95   £150

1972 ISSUE

Purple on multicolour. 182 x 99mm
Signature:
J. B. Burke £65   £100

ONE HUNDRED POUNDS

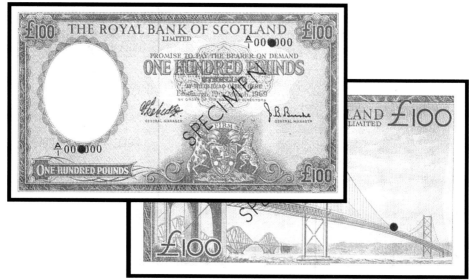

1969 ISSUE

Red on multicolour. 182 x 99mm
Signatures:
A. P. Robertson and J. B. Burke (1969) £200   £450

1972 ISSUE

Red on multicolour. 182 x 99mm
Signatures:
A. P. Robertson and J. B. Burke £150   £350

THE ROYAL BANK OF SCOTLAND PLC

ONE POUND

1982–86 ISSUES	EF	UNC

Green on multicolour. 135 x 67mm
Signatures:

	EF	UNC
Charles Winter (1982) (with sorting marks)	£5	£6
Charles Winter (1983–85) (without sorting marks)	£2	£6
Charles Winter (as Chief Executive) (1986)	£3	£4
R. M. Maiden (1986)	£3	£4

1987 ISSUE

Green on multicolour. 135 x 67mm
Signatures:

	EF	UNC
R. M. Maiden	£3	£3

1988 ISSUE

Green on multicolour. As above but reduced size. 127 x 65mm
Signatures:

	EF	UNC
R. M. Maiden (1988–90)	£3	£3
Charles Winter (1991)	£3	£3
George R. Mathewson (1992–93, 1996–97)	£3	£3
George R. Mathewson (as Group Chief Executive) (1999)	—	£2

The Royal Bank of Scotland plc. One pound (continued)   *EF*   *UNC*

1992 COMMEMORATIVE ISSUE—EUROPEAN SUMMIT

Green on multicolour with violet overprint. 127 x 65mm ....   —   £3

1994 REGULAR ISSUE

Green on multicolour. 127 x 65mm. No watermark £12   £22

1994 COMMEMORATIVE ISSUE—R. L. STEVENSON

Green on multicolour with violet overprint. 127 x 65mm ....   —   £3

1997 COMMEMORATIVE ISSUE—A. G. BELL

Green on multicolour with violet overprint. 127 x 65mm ....   —   £2

The Royal Bank of Scotland plc. One pound (continued)   *EF*   *UNC*

1999 COMMEMORATIVE ISSUE—SCOTTISH ASSEMBLY

Green on multicolour with violet overprint. 127 x 65mm   —   £2.50

FIVE POUNDS

1982–86 ISSUES

Blue on multicolour. 146 x 78mm
Signatures:

Charles Winter (1982–83) (with sorting marks)	£15	£50
Charles Winter (1984) (without sorting marks)	£15	£50
Charles Winter ("Managing Director" in large typeface) (1985)	£15	£45
R. M. Maiden (1986)	£12	£50

The Royal Bank of Scotland plc. Five pounds (continued)   *EF*   *UNC*

1987 ISSUE

Blue and blue-black on multicolour. 146 x 78mm
Signature:
R. M. Maiden £8   £22

1988 ISSUE

Blue and blue-black on multicolour. As above but reduced size 135 x 72mm
Signatures:
R. M. Maiden (1988–90) ....   —   £15
George R. Mathewson (1994–98) ....   —   £8
George R. Mathewson (as Group Chief Executive) (1999) ....   —   £8

TEN POUNDS

1982–86 ISSUES

Brown on multicolour. 158 x 89mm
Signatures:
Charles Winter (1982–85) £40   £90
R. M. Maiden (1986) £15   £40

The Royal Bank of Scotland plc. Ten pounds (continued)   *EF*   *UNC*

reverse

1987 ISSUE

Brown on multicolour. 158 x 89mm
Signature:
R. M. Maiden £12   £28

1992 ISSUE

Brown on multicolour. As above but size reduced 142 x 75mm
Signatures:
George R. Mathewson .... —   £14

Glamis Castle as depicted on the 1987 £10 note.

135

The Royal Bank of Scotland plc (continued)   *EF*   *UNC*

TWENTY POUNDS

1982–86 ISSUES

Purple on multicolour. 182 x 99mm
Signature: Charles Winter £35   £75

1987 ISSUE

Black and purple on multicolour. 182 x 99mm
Signatures:
R. M. Maiden .... —   £50

1991 ISSUE

Black and purple on multicolour. As above but reduced size 150 x 81mm
Signatures:
Charles Winter (1991) .... —   £45
George R. Mathewson (1992–98) .... —   £30
George R. Mathewson (as Group Executive) (1999) .... —   £28
    Queen Mother commemorative (2000) .... —   £28

The Royal Bank of Scotland. One pound (continued)   EF   UNC

ONE HUNDRED POUNDS

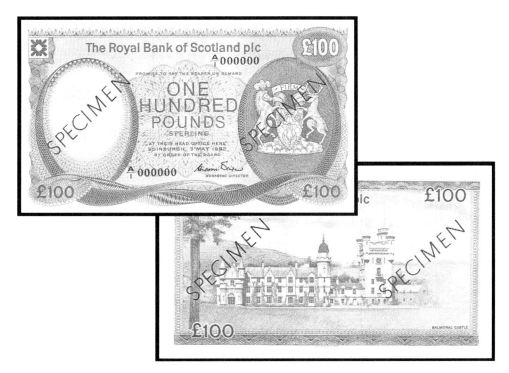

1982–86 ISSUES

Red on multicolour. 182 x 99mm
Signature: Charles Winter £125   £200

1987 ISSUE

Red on multicolour. 182 x 99mm
Signatures:
R. M. Maiden (1987–90) .... —   £200
George R. Mathewson (1992–98) .... —   £160

The Isle of Man

Banking in the Isle of Man dates from 1788 when Taubman and Goldie formed the Isle of Man Bank and produced notes of one guinea or five pounds. John Taubman later joined with George Quayle in forming the Isle of Man Banking Company in 1802. Various other private banks, many of them quite short-lived, appeared in the early 19th century and produced a number of distinctive notes, often for quite small amounts. This position was regularised by an Act of Tynwald in 1817 which abolished notes with a face value below a pound. The various permutations and combinations in the Isle of Man Bank are reflected in the different inscriptions on the notes issued throughout the 19th century. In the same period other banks which made a relatively brief impact included the Isle of Man & Liverpool joint-stock bank (1836-8), the Isle of Man Commercial Bank (1838-58) and the ill-fated Bank of Mona, actually a branch of the City of Glasgow Bank which opened in 1849 and continued until 1878 when the parent bank crashed. Its operations were then taken over by Dumbell's Bank, followed in 1882 by the Manx Bank. In addition, Manx branches of several English banks issued their own notes at various times up to 1961.

The reconstituted Isle of Man Bank, which became a limited company in 1926, continued to issue distinctive notes until 1961. In that year the note-issuing privilege was withdrawn from the private banks and notes issued by the Isle of Man government were substituted. The first series bore the Annigoni portrait of the Queen, but were followed from 1972 onwards by more up-to-date portraits alongside the three-legged emblem, with scenic vignettes on the reverse. The Isle of Man retained 10 shillings, and later 50p, notes long after they had been abandoned in Britain, and even had a plastic (Tyvek) pound note in the early 1980s. It is this latter series (from 1961) that is catalogued in this edition but it is hoped to include earlier issues in future editions.

An attractive note of the Isle of Man Bank Ltd.

ISLE OF MAN GOVERNMENT

TEN SHILLINGS

1961 ISSUE

Red with multicolour tints. 140 x 67mm
Signatures:

	EF	UNC
R. H. Garvey (1961–68)	£10	£30
P. H. G. Stallard (1969)	£8	£25

FIFTY NEW PENCE

1969 ISSUE

Blue with multicolour tints. 140 x 67mm
Signatures:

	EF	UNC
P. H. G. Stallard	£5	£12

1972 ISSUE

Blue with multicolour tints. 126 x 62mm
Signatures:

	EF	UNC
P. H. G. Stallard (1972)	£15	£35
John Paul (26mm) (1974–75)	£5	£10
John Paul (20mm) (1979)	£5	£10

1979 ISSUE

Blue with multicolour tints. 126 x 62mm
Signatures:

	EF	UNC
W. Dawson	—	£5

EF   UNC

ONE POUND

1961 ISSUE

Violet with multicolour tints. 151 x 72mm
Signatures:
R. H. Garvey (1961–67) £15   £50
P. H. G. Stallard (1967–70) £15   £45

1972 ISSUE

Violet with multicolour tints. 135 x 67mm
Signatures (Lieutenant Governor):
P. H. G. Stallard (1972) £15   £50
John Paul (26mm) (1974) £20   £65
John Paul (20mm) (1976–79) £3   £10

1979 ISSUE

Violet with multicolour tints. 135 x 67mm
Signature (Treasurer):
W. Dawson .... —   £8

1983 ISSUE

Green with multicolour tints. 135 x 67mm as before but on Tyvek (Bradvek) polymer
Signatures:
W. Dawson (M, N or P prefix) £3   £10

One pound (continued)   *EF*   *UNC*

1988 ISSUE

Violet with multicolour tints. Reverting to paper and original colour. 135 x 67mm
Signatures:
W. Dawson ....   —   £5

1990 ISSUE

Violet with multicolour tints. 128 x 64mm
Signatures:
W. Dawson (1990) ....   —   £5
J. A. Cashen (1991–) ....   —   £3

FIVE POUNDS

1961 ISSUE

Green and blue with multicolour tints. 140 x 85mm
Signatures:
R. H. Garvey (1961) £100   £550
P. H. G. Stallard (1968) £85   £300

1972 ISSUE

Blue and maroon with multicolour tints. 146 x 78mm
Signatures (Lieutenant Governor):
P. H. G. Stallard (1972) £25   £150
John Paul (1974–79) £25   £120

Five pounds (continued) *EF* *UNC*

1979 ISSUE

Blue and maroon with multicolour tints. 146 x 78mm
Signature (Treasurer):
W. Dawson £25 £120

1990 ISSUE

Mauve and blue with multicolour tints. 135 x 70mm
Signatures:
W. Dawson (Nov. 1991) £12 £30
J. A. Cashen (Dec. 1991–) £8 £15

TEN POUNDS

1972 ISSUE

Brown and green with multicolour tints. 151 x 84mm
Signatures (Lieutenant Governor):
P. H. G. Stallard (1972) £250 £750
John Paul (26mm) (1975) £100 £250

1979 ISSUE

Brown and green with multicolour tints. 151 x 84mm
Signature (Treasurer):
W. Dawson £25 £120

1990 ISSUE

Brown and green with multicolour tints. 141 x 76mm
Signatures:
W. Dawson (June 1991) So rare none seen .... — —
  B prefix design as above (151 x 84mm) only one known .... — —
J. A. Cashen (Aug. 1991–) £10 £25
J. A. Cashen (1998) (text without "Limited") .... — £15

EF   UNC

TWENTY POUNDS

1979 ISSUE

Red and brown with multicolour tints. 160 x 90mm
Signatures:
W. Dawson with Millennium Commemorative overprint £85   £200
W. Dawson without Millennium Commemorative overprint £50   £150

1990 ISSUE

Red and brown with multicolour tints. As above but reduced size 148 x 80mm
Signatures:
W. Dawson (June 1991) £65   £220
J. A. Cashen (Oct. 1991–) .... —   £50
J. A. Cashen (2000) (text without "Limited") .... —   £28

FIFTY POUNDS

1983 ISSUE

Blue and green with multicolour tints. 169 x 95mm
Signatures:
W. Dawson .... —   £85

The Channel Islands

In the Channel Islands notes have been produced by the private banks since 1797, while the States of Guernsey issued the first government notes in 1816. Twenty years elapsed before the States of Jersey followed suit, producing a large £5 note which was unusual in that it bore interest. Sets of notes, ranging from sixpence to £5, were issued by Guernsey and Jersey during the German occupation of World War II. The Jersey notes bore attractive vignettes on the reverse, based on watercolour paintings by the eminent local artist, Edmund Blampied.

Attractive notes are produced by the state banks in both bailiwicks to this day, the relatively plain issues of the immediate postwar period gradually giving way to much more pictorial motifs in the late 1960s and culminating in the present series, dating from the early 1980s, with greater prominence being given to local celebrities and historic scenes. Interestingly, Jersey has included portraits of Her Majesty the Queen, including the celebrated portrait by Pietro Annigoni on the pound note of 1963.

For this edition of the BANKNOTE YEARBOOK it has been decided to include only the banknote issues of the current reign and it is hoped to include earlier issues in future editions.

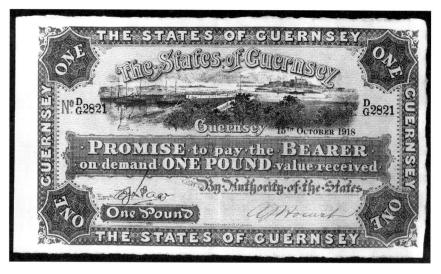

An early 20th century Guernsey note

GUERNSEY

TEN SHILLINGS

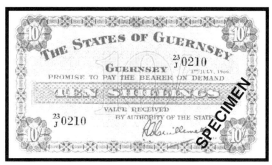

1945–52 ISSUE	*EF*	*UNC*

Lilac on light green. 139–142 x 81mm
Signatures:

H. E. Marquand	£150	£250
R. Guillemette	£150	£250

1953–66 ISSUE

Lilac on light green. 137–139 x 77–79mm
Signatures:

R. Guillemette	£20	£45

ONE POUND

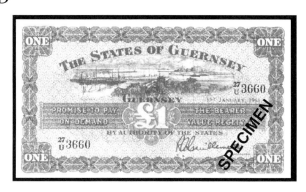

1945–52 ISSUE

Purple on green. 153–157 x 86–87mm
Signatures:

H. E. Marquand	£150	£200
R. Guillemette	£100	£150

1953–66 ISSUE

Purple on green. 151–153 x 85–86mm
Signatures:

R. Guillemette	£50	£110

Guernsey. One pound (continued)   *EF*   *UNC*

1969–75 ISSUE

Olive on pink and yellow. 134 x 73mm
Signatures:

	EF	UNC
R. Guillemette	£10	£30
A. W. Hodder	£5	£15
W. C. Bull	£5	£15

1980 ISSUE

Green and black on multicoloured underprint. (smaller) 135 x 67mm
Signatures:

	EF	UNC
W. C. Bull	£3	£12
M. J. Brown (signature in Black on H prefix only)	£2	£14

1990 ISSUE

Green and black on multicolour underprint. 128 x 65mm
Signatures:

	EF	UNC
M. J. Brown	—	£3
D. P. Trestain	—	£2

Guernsey (continued)   *EF*   *UNC*

FIVE POUNDS

1956–66 ISSUE

Green and blue. 155 x 89mm
Signature:
R. Guillemette £200   £400

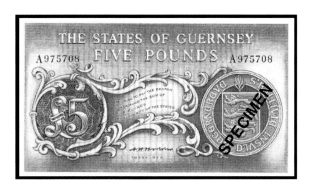

1969–75 ISSUE

Purple on light brown. 146 x 85mm
Signatures:
R. Guillemette £60   £130
A. W. Hodder £30   £80
W. C. Bull £25   £50

1980 ISSUE

Purple and brown on multicolour underprint. 146 x 78mm
Signature:
W. C. Bull £10   £25

1990 ISSUE

Purple and brown on multicolour underprint. As above but reduced size 136 x 70mm
Signatures:
M. J. Brown .... —   £15
D. P. Trestain .... —   £15

Guernsey. Five pounds (continued)   *EF*   *UNC*

1996 ISSUE

Purple and brown on multicolour underprint. 136 x 70mm
Signature:
D. P. Trestain ....   —   £10
D. P. Trestain (2000) MM prefix, Millennium issue ....   —   £12

TEN POUNDS

1969–75 ISSUE

Blue and green. 149 x 79mm
Signature:
A. W. Hodder £90   £190

1980 ISSUE

Blue and green. 151 x 85mm
Signatures:
W. C. Bull £18   £50
M. J. Brown £18   £50

Guernsey. Ten pounds (continued)   *EF*   *UNC*

1992 ISSUE

Purple and blue. 142 x 75mm
Signatures:
M. J. Brown (blue signature) £45

1994–96 ISSUE

Violet and blue. 142 x 75mm
Signatures:
D. P. Trestain £10   £20

TWENTY POUNDS

1980 ISSUE

Red and brown. 161 x 90mm
Signature:

	EF	UNC
W. C. Bull	£35	£75
M. J. Brown	£28	£65

1990–91 ISSUE

Red and brown. 149 x 80mm
Signatures:

M. J. Brown	—	£40
D. P. Trestain	—	£45

1994–96 ISSUE

Red, pink and brown. 149 x 80mm
Signatures:

D. P. Trestain	—	£35

FIFTY POUNDS

1994–96 ISSUE

Brown, green and blue. 156 x 85mm
Signatures:
D. P. Trestain ....   —   £75

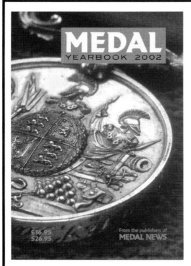

JERSEY

	EF	*UNC*

TEN SHILLINGS

1963 ISSUE

Brown on multicolour underprint. 140 x 71mm
Signature:
F. N. Padgham £7   £15

ONE POUND

1963 ISSUE

Green on multicolour underprint. 151 x 77mm
Signature:
F. N. Padgham £18   £45
J. Clennett £15   £35

Jersey. One pound (continued)   *EF*   *UNC*

1976 ISSUE

Blue on multicolour underprint. 134 x 67mm
Signature:
J. Clennett £3   £5
Leslie May £2   £4

1989 ISSUE

Green and violet on multicolour underprint. 128 x 65mm.
Signature:
Leslie May ....   —   £2

1993 ISSUE

Green and violet on multicolour underprint. As above but with solid numeral of value. 128 x 65mm.
Signature:
George Baird ....   —   £2
Ian Black ....   —   £2

1995 COMMEMORATIVE ISSUE

Green and purple on multicolour underprint. 128 x 65mm
Overprinted "50th Anniversary of the Liberation of Jersey"
Signature:
George Baird. ....   —   £5

EF   *UNC*

FIVE POUNDS

1963 ISSUE

Red on multicolour underprint. 140 x 85mm
Signature:
F. N. Padgham £80   £220
J. Clennett £15   £35

1976 ISSUE

Brown on multicolour underprint. 146 x 78mm
Signature:
J. Clennett £12   £25
Leslie May £7   £18

1989 ISSUE

Red on multicolour underprint. 135 x 70mm
Signature:
Leslie May ....   —   £12

1993 ISSUE

Red on multicolour underprint. As above but with solid numeral of value. 135 x 70mm
Signature:
George Baird ....   —   £12

Jersey (continued)   *EF*   *UNC*

TEN POUNDS

1971 ISSUE

Purple on multicolour underprint. 151 x 85mm
Signature: J. Clennett £20   £45

1976 ISSUE

Green on multicolour underprint. 151 x 85mm
Signatures:
J. Clennett £18   £40
Leslie May £15   £30

1989 ISSUE

Brown on multicolour underprint. 142 x 76mm
Signature: Leslie May ....   —   £20

1993 ISSUE

Brown on multicolour underprint. As above but with solid numeral of value. 142 x 76mm
Signature: George Baird ....   —   £16

TWENTY POUNDS

1976 ISSUE

Red on multicolour underprint. 160 x 90mm
Signature:
J. Clennett £35 £85
Leslie May £30 £85

1989 ISSUE

Blue on multicolour underprint. 149 x 80mm
Signature:
Leslie May .... — £40

1993 ISSUE

Blue on multicolour underprint. As above but with solid numeral of value. 149 x 80mm
Signature:
George Baird .... — £30

Jersey (continued)   *EF*   *UNC*

FIFTY POUNDS

1989 ISSUE

Black on multicolour underprint. 156 x 85mm
Signature:
Leslie May ....   —   £110

1993 ISSUE

Black on multicolour underprint. As above but with solid numeral of value. 156 x 85mm
Signature:
George Baird ....   —   £75

Ireland

Ireland was a relative latecomer to banking, the first notes of the Bank of Ireland being introduced in 1783. Thereafter the history of banking paralleled that of Scotland, with a number of private banks in the early 19th century which, as a result of mergers and amalgamations, resulted in half a dozen major banks still producing distinctive notes at the turn of the century.

The situation was complicated by the political developments which led to the establishment of the Irish Free State and the province of Northern Ireland in 1921. The Belfast Banking Company, whose notes circulated through the whole of Ireland, confined its activities to Northern Ireland from 1922 onwards. On the other hand, the Bank of Ireland, which was traditionally based in Dublin, was obliged to produce separate issues from 1929 onwards for Northern Ireland and the Irish Free State, while both the Provincial Bank of Ireland and the Ulster Bank likewise had distinctive issues for the Free State and Northern Ireland in the same period.

In the Irish Free State, the government established a Currency Commission in 1927 under whose auspices notes, inscribed in English and Irish, were issued from 1928 onwards, notable on account of the portrait of Hazel, Lady Lavery in the guise of an Irish colleen. The inscriptions in these notes were altered in 1938 from Irish Free State (Saorstát Éireann) to Ireland (Eire), following the constitutional changes of that year. In addition the Currency Commission produced distinctive notes, showing a farmer ploughing, with the names of one or other of the eight "shareholder" banks inscribed at the foot: the Bank of Ireland, the Hibernian Bank, the Munster & Leinster Bank, the National Bank, the Northern Bank, the Provincial Bank, the Royal Bank and the Ulster Bank. These notes were replaced from 1943 onwards by the notes of the Central Bank of Ireland, which at first retained the Lady Lavery portrait, but since 1976 have used historic scenes and personalities.

Distinctive notes for circulation in Northern Ireland have been produced by the Bank of Ireland, the Belfast Banking Company and the National, Northern, Provincial and Ulster banks and it is interesting to note that the Bank of Ireland even produced a commemorative £20 in 1983 to celebrate its bicentenary. Generally speaking, the notes of Northern Ireland have always been much more varied in their designs and subject matter. Bank amalgamations led to the formation of the Allied Irish Banks Limited whose notes, similar to the last issue of the Provincial Bank, were introduced in January 1982.

For this issue of the BANKNOTE YEARBOOK it has been decided to catalogue only the modern issues of Northern Ireland and the Republic of Ireland.

NORTHERN IRELAND

ALLIED IRISH BANKS LTD.
(later becomes Allied Irish Banks PLC)

	EF	UNC

ONE POUND

1982 ISSUE

Green on multicoloured underprint. 134 x 66mm
Signature:
P. O'Keiffe £5   £15

FIVE POUNDS

1982 ISSUE

Blue and purple. 146 x 78mm
Signature:
P. O'Keiffe £15   £30

TEN POUNDS

1982 ISSUE

Brown and green. 151 x 84mm
Signature:
P. O'Keiffe. £22   £45

TWENTY POUNDS

1982 ISSUE

Purple and green. 160 x 90mm
Signature:
P. O'Keiffe £45   £90

ONE HUNDRED POUNDS

1982 ISSUE

Black and green. 170 x 95mm
Signature:
P. O'Keiffe £145   £300

ALLIED IRISH BANKS PLC
(later becomes First Trust Bank)

	EF	UNC

FIVE POUNDS

1987–88 ISSUE
Blue and purple on multicoloured underprint
Signature:
G. B. Scanlon .... — £25

TEN POUNDS

1987–88 ISSUE
Brown and green
Signature:
G. B. Scanlon. .... — £35

TWENTY POUNDS

1987–88 ISSUE
Purple and green
Signature:
G. B. Scanlon. .... — £55

ONE HUNDRED POUNDS

1987–88 ISSUE
Black and green
Signature:
G. B. Scanlon. .... — £300

BANK OF IRELAND (BELFAST)

1990–95 issue £10

ONE POUND

1929 ISSUE	*VF*	*EF*
Black on blue and green underprint. 151 x 72mm		
Signature:		
J. H. Craig (1929)	£25	£60
G. W. Frazer (1933–36)	£18	£45
81936 ISSUE		
Black on blue and green underprint. 151 x 72mm		
Signature:		
G. W. Frazer (1936–40)	£20	£36
H. J. Adams (1942–43)	£15	£30
1967 ISSUE		
Black and green on purple underprint. 151 x 72mm		
Signature:		
W. E. Guthrie	£8	£15
1971–74 ISSUE		
Black and green on purple underprint. 134 x 66mm		
Signature:		
H. H. M. Chestnutt (1972)	£3 •	£12
A. S. J. O'Neill (1977)	—	£10
1980–89 ISSUE		
Black and green on purple underprint. 134 x 66mm.		
Signature:		
A. S. J. O'Neill (STERLING added below central denomination)	—	£5

FIVE POUNDS

1929 ISSUE		
Red and orange. 151 x 72mm		
Signature:		
J. H. Craig (1929)	£35	£95
G. W. Frazer (1935–40)	£30	£65
H. J. Adams (1942–43)	£25	£45
S. E. Skuce (1958)	£14	£35

Bank of Ireland (Belfast). Five pounds (continued)	*EF*	*UNC*

1967 ISSUE

Violet. 140 x 85mm
Signatures:

W. E. Guthrie (1967)	£20	£50
H. H. M. Chestnutt (1968)	£18	£45

1971–74 ISSUE

Blue on green and purple underprint. 146 x 78mm
Signatures:

H. H. M. Chestnutt (1971)	£15	£30
A. S. J. O'Neill (1977)	£10	£25

1980–89 ISSUE

Blue on green and purple underprint. 146 x 78mm
Signatures:

A. S. J. O'Neill (1980)	£9	£18
D. F. Harrison (1989)	£10	£20

1990–95 ISSUE

Blue and purple on multicoloured underprint. 146 x 78mm
Signatures:

D. F. Harrison (1989)	—	£10
McGinn (1995–)	—	£10

TEN POUNDS

1929 ISSUE

Blue and green. 151 x 72mm
Signature:

	VF	*EF*
J. H. Craig (1929)	£85	£175
H. J. Adams (1942–43)	£25	£85

1967 ISSUE

Brown and yellow. 150 x 93mm
Signature:

	EF	*UNC*
W. E. Guthrie	£25	£100

1971–74 ISSUE

Brown on multicoloured underprint. 151 x 84mm
Signatures:

H. H. M. Chestnutt (1971)	£15	£50
A. S. J. O'Neill (1977)	£12	£25

1980–89 ISSUE

Brown on multicoloured underprint. 151 x 84mm
Signatures:

A. S. J. O'Neill (1980)	£15	£30
D. F. Harrison (1989)	£18	£35

1990–954 ISSUE

Purple on multicoloured underprint. 151 x 84mm
Signatures:

D. F. Harrison	—	£20
1995–98 McGinn - Y last (1995–98)	—	£20
McGinn AA - (1998–)	—	£20

TWENTY POUNDS

1929 ISSUE

	VF	*EF*

Black on orange and green. 160 x 90mm
Signature:

J. H. Craig	£300	£500

Bank of Ireland (Belfast). Twenty pounds (continued)   EF   UNC

1980–89 ISSUE
Brown on multicoloured underprint. 160 x 90mm
Signatures:
A. S. J. O'Neill (1980) £20   £50
A. S. J. O'Neill. With Bank Centenary commemorative overprint (1983) £115   £250
D. F. Harrison (1989) £35   £65

1990–94 ISSUE
Green and brown on multicoloured underprint. 148 x 80mm
Signature:
D. F. Harrison .... —   £40
McGinn (1995) .... —   £30

FIFTY POUNDS

1990–95 ISSUE
Brown and green on multicoloured underprint. 170 x 95mm
Signature:
D. F. Harrison .... —   £110
1995 McGinn (1995) .... —   £75

ONE HUNDRED POUNDS

1971–74 ISSUE
Red on multicoloured underprint. 170 x 95mm
Signatures:
H. H. M. Chestnutt (1974) .... —   £275
A. S. J. O'Neill (1978) .... —   £225

1980–89 ISSUE
Red on multicoloured underprint. 170 x 95mm (STERLING added)
Signatures:
A. S. J. O'Neill (1980) .... —   £200
D. F. Harrison (1989) .... —   £185

1990–95 ISSUE
Red on multicoloured underprint. 170 x 95mm (STERLING added)
Signature:
D. F. Harrison (1989) .... —   £185
McGinn (1995) .... —   £175

BELFAST BANKING COMPANY LTD.

	VF	EF

ONE POUND

1922 ISSUE

Black on blue underprint. 151 x 72mm

Black serial number (1922–28)	£55	£125
Red serial number (1939–40)	£15	£30

FIVE POUNDS

1922 ISSUE

Blue on red underprint. 151 x 72mm

Black serial number (1923–27)...	£45	£150
Red serial number (1928–42)	£28	£50
Red serial number (1966)	£15	£30

TEN POUNDS

1922 ISSUE

Black on green underprint. 151 x 72mm

Black serial number (1923)..	£75	£185
Green serial number (1929–43)..	£55	£125
Green serial number (1963–65)..	£30	£75

TWENTY POUNDS

1922 ISSUE

Brown on mauve underprint

Black serial number (1923)..	£95	£225
Mauve serial number (1939–40)	£75	£185
Black serial number (1943)..	£65	£150
Black serial number (1965)..	£55	£150

Belfast Banking Company Ltd. (continued)   *VF*   *EF*

FIFTY POUNDS

1922 ISSUE

Brown on mauve underprint
Black serial number (1923)	£125	£250
Yellow serial number (1939–40)	£100	£200
Black serial number (1943)	£100	£200
Black serial number (1963)	£85	£225

ONE HUNDRED POUNDS

1922 ISSUE

Brown on red underprint
1923 issue	£185	£300
1939–43 issue	£125	£250
1963 issue	£125	£250
1968 issue	£125	£250

FIRST TRUST BANK

                                                                            EF   *UNC*

TEN POUNDS

1994 ISSUE
Brown and purple. 151 x 84mm .... —   £15

TWENTY POUNDS

1994 ISSUE
Red-brown and purple. 148 x 80mm .... —   £30

FIFTY POUNDS

1994 ISSUE
Black, green and blue. 170 x 95mm .... —   £75

ONE HUNDRED POUNDS

1994 ISSUE
Brown and black. 170 x 95mm .... —   £150

NATIONAL BANK (BELFAST)

Hibernia issue

ONE POUND

VF   EF

1929 (ARMS) ISSUE
Black on green underprint. £125   £275

1937 (HIBERNIA) ISSUE
Black and green. £25   £100

FIVE POUNDS

1929 (ARMS) ISSUE
Blue on brown underprint. £175   £350

1937 (HIBERNIA) ISSUE
Blue and brown £55   £150

1942 ISSUE
Blue and brown £45   £140

TEN POUNDS

1929 (ARMS) ISSUE
Green on brown underprint. £250   £450

1937 (HIBERNIA) ISSUE
Green and brown £75   £150

1942 ISSUE
Green and brown £75   £150

1959ISSUE
Green and pink £55   £100

TWENTY POUNDS

1937 ISSUE
Brown and green £200   £400

1942 ISSUE
Brown and green £185   £350

1959 ISSUE
Brown and green £200   £400

NORTHERN BANK LTD.

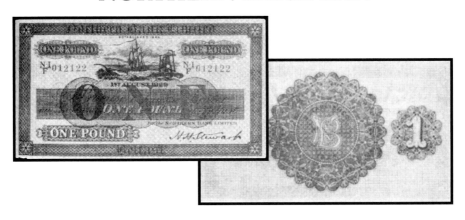

ONE POUND

	EF	UNC
1929 ISSUE (as above)		
Black and blue		
Red serial number (1929)	£25	£75
Black serial number (1940)	£15	£35
Black serial number (1968)	—	—
1970 ISSUE (Dockyard design)		
Green on pink.		
Signatures:		
Wilson (1970)...	£6*	£15
Gabbey (1971)	**£5**	**£12**
Ervin (1978)..	£5	£10

FIVE POUNDS

1929 ISSUE (similar design to £1 above)		
Black and blue	£50	£125
1930–43 ISSUE (similar design to £1 above)		
Black and green		
Red serial number (1937)	£45	£100
Black serial number (1940–43)	£25	£75
1968 ISSUE (similar design to £1 above)		
Black and green	£15	£40
1970 ISSUE (Dockyard design)		
Blue	£10	£30
1988 ISSUE (Trolley car and Station design)		
Blue	£10	£30
2000 ISSUE (illustrated overleaf)		
Blue on polymer in a vertical format	—	£8
In Presentation Wallet	—	£15

Northern Bank. Five pounds (continued)   *EF*   *UNC*

Northern Bank's first polymer note.

TEN POUNDS

1930–43 ISSUE (similar design to £1)

Black and red

Red serial number (1930–Jan. 1940)	£65	£150
Black serial number (Aug. 1940)	£55	£130
Red serial number (1942–43)	£40	£95
Imprint on reverse (Aug. 1968)	£30	£60

1970 ISSUE (Dockyard design)

Brown	£15	£50

1988 ISSUE (Automobile and Cyclist design)

Brown and red	£15	£35 [a]

1997 ISSUE (illustrated)

Brown and red	—	£16

Northern Bank (continued) · *EF* · *UNC*

TWENTY POUNDS

1970 ISSUE (Dockyard design)
Mauve.
Signature: Wilson £25 £90

1988 ISSUE (Ferguson and Tractor design)
Brown and red.
Signature: Tomens £32 £65

1996 ISSUE (Modernised Ferguson and Tractor design)
Brown and violet.
Signatures:
Wright (1996) .... — —
Savage (1997) £25 £50
Price (1999) .... — £30

FIFTY POUNDS

1930–43 ISSUE (similar design to £1)
Black and blue £125 £250

1968 ISSUE (with monogram)
Black and blue £100 £200

1970 ISSUE (Dockyard design)
Orange £75 £150

1988 ISSUE (Personalities)
Black and green.
Signature: Torrens £55 £120

1999 ISSUE (illustrated)
Black and green .... — —

ONE HUNDRED POUNDS

1930–43 ISSUE (similar design to £1)
Black and blue £175   £275

1968 ISSUE (with monogram)
Black and blue £150   £250

1970 ISSUE (Dockyard design)
Black and red .... —   £150

1988 ISSUE (Personalities)
Black, blue and mauve .... —   £120

1999 ISSUE (illustrated)
Black and lilac .... —   £150

PROVINCIAL BANK OF IRELAND LTD.
(BELFAST)

ONE POUND

	VF	EF

1929 ISSUE

Black and green
Signatures:

H. Robertson (1929)	£75	£175
F. S. Forde (1932–34)	£60	£140

1935–38 ISSUE

Green
Signatures:

F. S. Forde (1935–36)	£40	£100
G. A. Kennedy (1936–46)	£40	£80

1954 ISSUE (illustrated)

	EF	UNC

Green.
Signature:

S. J. Shaw	£20	£75

1968 ISSUE

Green. As above but reduced size	£10	£25

1977 ISSUE

Green
Signature:

J. G. McClay	£5	£12
F. H. Hollway	£3	£6

FIVE POUNDS

1929 ISSUE

	VF	EF

Blue
Signatures:

H. Robertson (1929–31)	£110	£225
F. S. Forde (1936)	£60	£160

Provincial Bank of Ireland. Five pounds (continued)	*VF*	*EF*

1936–46 ISSUE
Black and brown
Signature:

G. A. Kennedy	£45	£125

1948–52 ISSUE
Black and brown on pink underprint
Signature:

H. W. M. Clarke	£20	£40

1954 ISSUE	*EF*	*UNC*

Brown
Signature:

S. J. Shaw	£20	£40

1977 ISSUE
Blue and mauve
Signature:

J. G. McClay	£8	£15
F. H. Hollway	£8	£15

TEN POUNDS

1929 ISSUE	*VF*	*EF*

Brown
Signatures:

H. Robertson (1929)	£150	£250
F. S. Forde (1934)	£100	£180

1936–46 ISSUE
Brown
Signature:

G. A. Kennedy	£80	£150

1948–52 ISSUE
Brown
Signature:

H. W. M. Clarke £65	£120	

1977 ISSUE	*EF*	*UNC*

Brown and green
Signature:

J. G. McClay	£20	£50
F. H. Hollway	£18	£45

ULSTER BANK LTD. (BELFAST)

The early issues use a variety of handwritten signatures.

	VF	EF

ONE POUND

1929 ISSUE
Black and blue.
Hand-signed. Reverse blank £35 £85

1935–36 ISSUE (illustrated)
Black and blue
Hand-signed. Building on reverse £25 £85

1939–41 ISSUE
Black and blue
Hand-signed. Building in frame on reverse (1939–40) £20 £65
Printed signature (1956) £20 £50

1966–70 ISSUE
Black and blue. New design
Printed signature £5 £10

1971–82 ISSUE
Black and blue.
Printed signature £2 £4

FIVE POUNDS

1929 ISSUE
Black and green
Hand-signed. Reverse blank £55 £110

1935–36 ISSUE
Black and green
Hand-signed. Building on reverse £45 £90

1939–41 ISSUE
Black and green
Hand-signed. Building in frame on reverse (1939–43) £25 £55
Printed signature (1956) £55 £110

Ulster Bank Ltd (Belfast). Five pounds (continued)   *EF*   *UNC*

1966–70 ISSUE
Brown on multicoloured underprint. New design
Printed signature £15   £40

1971–82 ISSUE
Brown on multicoloured underprint.
Signatures:
H. E. O'B. Traill £12   £35
R. W. Hamilton £10   £25
V. Chambers £10   £25

1989–90 ISSUE
Brown on multi-coloured underprint
Signatures:
D. Went .... —   £15
Wilson (1998) .... —   £8

TEN POUNDS

1929 ISSUE	*VF*	*EF*

Black and red
Hand-signed. Reverse blank £75   £175

1935–36 ISSUE
Black and red
Hand-signed. Building on reverse £50   £110

1939–41 ISSUE
Black and red
Hand-signed. Building in frame on reverse £60   £100

1966–70 ISSUE
Green on multicoloured underprint. New design
Printed signature: Jno. J. A. Leitch £25   £80

1971–82 ISSUE
Green on multicoloured underprint
Signatures:
H. E. O'B. Traill £20   £75
R. W. Hamilton £15   £65
V. Chambers £12   £50

1989–90 ISSUE
Green on multicoloured underprint
Signature: D. Went .... —   £25

Ulster Bank Ltd (Belfast). Ten pounds (continued)   *EF*   *UNC*

1996 ISSUE

Green on multicoloured underprint ....   —   £20
Signature: R. Kells (1997) ....   —   £25

TWENTY POUNDS

	VF	EF
1929 ISSUE		
Black and blue		
Hand-signed. Reverse blank	£125	£250
1939–41 ISSUE		
Black and blue		
Hand-signed. Building in frame on reverse	£75	£150
1966–70 ISSUE		
Mauve on multicoloured underprint. New design		
Printed signature	£45	£85
1971–82 ISSUE		
Mauve on multicoloured underprint.	£22	£55
1989–90 ISSUE		
Mauve on multicoloured underprint	—	£35

	EF	UNC
1996 ISSUE		
Mauve on multicoloured underprint.	—	£26

Ulster Bank Ltd (Belfast) (continued)   *VF*   *EF*

FIFTY POUNDS

1929 ISSUE
Black and blue
Hand-signed. Reverse blank £190   £300

1939–41 ISSUE
Black and blue
Hand-signed. Building in frame on reverse £150   £250

1971–82 ISSUE
Brown on multicoloured underprint. .... —   £75

1996 ISSUE   *EF*   *UNC*
Brown on multicoloured underprint. .... —   £75

ONE HUNDRED POUNDS

1929 ISSUE   *VF*   *EF*
Black and blue
Hand-signed. Reverse blank £200   £450

1939–41 ISSUE
Black and blue
Hand-signed. Building in frame on reverse £175   £350

1971–82 ISSUE
Red on multicoloured underprint. .... —   £150

1996 ISSUE   *EF*   *UNC*
Red on multicoloured underprint .... —   £170

REPUBLIC OF IRELAND

CURRENCY COMMISSION
(Consolidated banknotes) (1929–41)

Designs for the notes issued by the eight Banks under the auspices of the
Currency Commission are virtually identical except for the values, titles and
signatures. Notes of the Bank of Ireland, as representative of the design, are
illustrated below and in colour on page 195.

The "Ploughman" series obverse

THE BANK OF IRELAND

	VF	EF

ONE POUND

1929 ISSUE

Green on orange and mauve underprint. 151 x 84mm
Signatures:

	VF	EF
Joseph Brennan and J. A. Gargan (1929–38)	£85	£250
Joseph Brennan and H. J. Johnson (1939–40)	£100	£275
Specimen note	—	£350

FIVE POUNDS

1929 ISSUE

Brown on green and mauve underprint. 165 x 92mm
Signatures:

	VF	EF
Joseph Brennan and J. A. Gargan (1929–31)	£200	£350
Joseph Brennan and H. J. Johnson (1939)	£250	£400
Specimen note	—	£550

TEN POUNDS

1929 ISSUE

Blue on green and mauve underprint. 190 x 108mm
Signatures:

	VF	EF
Joseph Brennan and J. A. Gargan	£425	£750
Specimen note	—	£650

£20, £50 and £100 notes exist only as Bank of Ireland Specimens (value ca. £1,500 each).
No issued notes remain.

HIBERNIAN BANK LTD.

ONE POUND
1929 ISSUE
Green on orange and mauve underprint. 151 x 84mm
Signatures:
Joseph Brennan and H. J. Campbell (1929–39) £100   £250
Joseph Brennan and A. K. Hodges (1939–40) £125   £350

FIVE POUNDS
1929 ISSUE
Brown on green and mauve underprint. 165 x 92mm
Signatures:
Joseph Brennan and H. J. Campbell (1929–May 1939) .... £200 ●   £350
Joseph Brennan and A. K. Hodges (Sept. 1939) (probably never issued) ....   —   —

TEN POUNDS
1929 ISSUE
Blue on green and mauve underprint. 190 x 108mm
Signatures:
Joseph Brennan and H. J. Campbell £500   £850

MUNSTER & LEINSTER BANK LTD.

ONE POUND
1929 ISSUE
Green on orange and mauve underprint. 151 x 84mm
Signatures:
Joseph Brennan and J. L. Gubbins (1929–35) .... £90   £200 ●
Joseph Brennan and A. E. Hosford (1936–40) £90   £200

FIVE POUNDS
1929 ISSUE
Brown on green and mauve underprint. 165 x 92mm
Signatures:
Joseph Brennan and J. L. Gubbins (1929–33) £175   £350
Joseph Brennan and A. E. Hosford (1938–39) £175   £350

TEN POUNDS
1929 ISSUE
Blue on green and mauve underprint. 190 x 108mm
Signatures:
Joseph Brennan and J. L. Gubbins (1929–31) £450   £700
Joseph Brennan and A. E. Hosford (1938–39) £450   £700

NATIONAL BANK LTD.

ONE POUND
1929 ISSUE
Green on orange and mauve underprint. 151 x 84mm
Signatures:
Joseph Brennan and H. A. Russell (1929–39) £85 £250

FIVE POUNDS
1929 ISSUE
Brown on green and mauve underprint. 165 x 92mm
Signatures:
Joseph Brennan and H. A. Russell (1929–May 1939) £200 £350

TEN POUNDS
1929 ISSUE
Blue on green and mauve underprint. 190 x 108mm
Signatures:
Joseph Brennan and J. L. Gubbins (1929–39)... £450 £700

NORTHERN BANK LTD.

ONE POUND
1929 ISSUE
Green on orange and mauve underprint. 151 x 84mm
Signatures:
Joseph Brennan and S. W. Knox (1929) £400 £600
Joseph Brennan and H. H. Stewart (1931–33) £300 £400

FIVE POUNDS
1929 ISSUE
Brown on green and mauve underprint. 165 x 92mm
Signatures:
Joseph Brennan and S. W. Knox (1929) £600 £1000
oseph Brennan and H. H. Stewart (1931–33) £300 £600

TEN POUNDS
1929 ISSUE
Blue on green and mauve underprint. 190 x 108mm
Signatures:
Joseph Brennan and S. W. Knox (1929) £1000 £1400

PROVINCIAL BANK OF IRELAND LTD.

ONE POUND

1929 ISSUE

Green on orange and mauve underprint. 151 x 84mm
Signatures:

Joseph Brennan and Hume Robertson (1929)	£110	£275
Joseph Brennan and F. S. Forde (1931–36)	£90	£250
Joseph Brennan and G. A. Kennedy (1937–40)	£90	£250

FIVE POUNDS

1929 ISSUE

Brown on green and mauve underprint. 165 x 92mm
Signatures:

Joseph Brennan and Hume Robertson (1929)	£275	£450
Joseph Brennan and F. S. Forde (1931–36)	£225	£400
Joseph Brennan and G. A. Kennedy (1937–40)	£225	£400

TEN POUNDS

1929 ISSUE

Blue on green and mauve underprint. 190 x 108mm
Signatures:

Joseph Brennan and Hume Robertson (1929)	£400	£650
Joseph Brennan and F. S. Forde (1931–36)	£400	£650
Joseph Brennan and G. A. Kennedy (1937–40)	£400	£650

ROYAL BANK OF IRELAND LTD.

ONE POUND

1929 ISSUE

Green on orange and mauve underprint. 151 x 84mm
Signatures:

Joseph Brennan and G. A. Stanley (1929)	£120	£275
Joseph Brennan and D. R. Mack (1931–39)	£100	£250
Joseph Brennan and J. Wilson(1939)	£120	£275

FIVE POUNDS

1929 ISSUE

Brown on green and mauve underprint. 165 x 92mm
Signatures:

Joseph Brennan and G. A. Stanley (1929)	£250	£450
Joseph Brennan and D. R. Mack (1931–39)	£200	£400

TEN POUNDS

1929 ISSUE

Blue on green and mauve underprint. 190 x 108mm
Signatures:

Joseph Brennan and G. A. Stanley (1929–31)	£550	£1000

Currency Commission (Consolidated banknotes) (continued)   *VF*   *EF*

ULSTER BANK LTD.

ONE POUND

1929 ISSUE

Green on orange and mauve underprint. 151 x 84mm
Signatures:

Joseph Brennan and C. W. Patton (1929–39)	£200	£400
Joseph Brennan and C. W. Lester (1939–40)	£200	£400

FIVE POUNDS

1929 ISSUE

Brown on green and mauve underprint. 165 x 92mm
Signatures:

Joseph Brennan and C. W. Patton (1929–39)	£300	£550
Joseph Brennan and C. W. Lester (1939)	£300	£550

TEN POUNDS

1929 ISSUE

Blue on green and mauve underprint. 190 x 108mm
Signatures:

Joseph Brennan and C. W. Patton (1929–39)	£550	£850
Joseph Brennan and C. W. Lester (1939)	£550	£850

Reverses of the three issued notes of the "Ploughman" series. (These illustrations of Specimen notes are from "Irish Government Paper Money from 1928" by Mártan Mac Devitt.)

SERIES A
"LADY LAVERY" NOTES (1928–77)

Designs for the notes issued under the auspices of the Currency Commission Irish Free State, the Currency Commission of Ireland and the Central Bank of Ireland are virtually identical except for the values, titles and signatures. Notes of the Central Bank of Ireland, as representative of the design, are illustrated below and in colour on page 195.

The "Lady Lavery" low denomination series obverse

	VF	EF

CURRENCY COMMISSION IRISH FREE STATE

TEN SHILLINGS

1928 ISSUE
Orange on green and mauve underprint. 138 x 78mm
Signatures:
Joseph Brennan and J. J. McElligott

	VF	EF
Fractional prefix—Letter over Number (1928)	£125	£250
Straight prefix—Number/Number/Letter (1929–37)	£85	£150

ONE POUND

1928 ISSUE
Green on pink and yellow underprint. 151 x 84mm
Signatures:
Joseph Brennan and J. J. McElligott

	VF	EF
Fractional prefix—Letter over Number (1928)	£110	£200•
Straight prefix—Number/Number/Letter (1930–37)	£95•	£175

FIVE POUNDS

1928 ISSUE
Brown on yellow and mauve underprint. 166 x 92mm
Signatures:
Joseph Brennan and J. J. McElligott

	VF	EF
Fractional prefix—Letter over Number (1928)	£175	£300
Straight prefix—Number/Number/Letter (1932–37)	£125	£250•

Series A, "Lady Lavery". Currency Commission Irish Free State (continued)	*VF*	*EF*

TEN POUNDS

1928 ISSUE

Blue on green and mauve underprint. 189 x 107mm
Signatures:
Joseph Brennan and J. J. McElligott

Fractional prefix—Letter over Number (1928)	£375	£500
Straight prefix—Number/Number/Letter (1932–33)	£200	£500

TWENTY POUNDS

1928 ISSUE

Red on orange and mauve underprint. 203 x 144mm
Signatures:
Joseph Brennan and J. J. McElligott .... £600 | —

FIFTY POUNDS

1928 ISSUE

Mauve on yellow underprint. 203 x 114mm
Signatures:
Joseph Brennan and J. J. McElligott .... £600 | £1000

ONE HUNDRED POUNDS

1928 ISSUE

Black on yellow and mauve underprint. 203 x 114mm
Signatures:
Joseph Brennan and J. J. McElligott .... £600 | £1200

CURRENCY COMMISSION IRELAND

TEN SHILLINGS

1938–42 ISSUE

Orange on green and mauve underprint. 138 x 78mm
Signatures:

Joseph Brennan and J. J. McElligott (1938–39)	£85	£150
Joseph Brennan and J. J. McElligott (1940–41)	£65	£85

ONE POUND

1938–42 ISSUE

Green on pink and yellow underprint. 151 x 84mm
Signatures:

Joseph Brennan and J. J. McElligott (1939)	£90	£125
Joseph Brennan and J. J. McElligott (1941–42)	£75	£100

FIVE POUNDS

1938–42 ISSUE

Brown on yellow and mauve underprint. 166 x 92mm
Signatures:

Joseph Brennan and J. J. McElligott (1938–39)	£90	£150
Joseph Brennan and J. J. McElligott (1940–42)	£80	£150

Series A, "Lady Lavery". Currency Commission Ireland (continued)   *VF*   *EF*

TEN POUNDS

1938–42 ISSUE

Blue on green and mauve underprint. 189 x 107mm
Signatures:

Joseph Brennan and J. J. McElligott (1938–40)	£100	£150
Joseph Brennan and J. J. McElligott (1941–42)	£150	£200

CENTRAL BANK OF IRELAND

TEN SHILLINGS

1943–77 ISSUE

Orange on green and mauve underprint. 138 x 78mm
Signatures:

Joseph Brennan and J. J. McElligott (1943–44)	£55	£75
Joseph Brennan and J. J. McElligott (1945–50)	£35	£50
Joseph Brennan and J. J. McElligott (1951–52)	£15	£35
J. J. McElligott and K. Redmond (1955)	£30	£80
J. J. McElligott and T. K. Whitaker (1957–59)	£10	£20
M. Ó Muimhneacháin and T. K. Whitaker (1962–68)	£5	£15

ONE POUND

1943–77 ISSUE

Green on pink and yellow underprint. 151 x 84mm
Signatures:

Joseph Brennan and J. J. McElligott (1943–44)	£50	£65
Joseph Brennan and J. J. McElligott (1945–50)	£20	£35
Joseph Brennan and J. J. McElligott (1951–52)	£12	£30
J. J. McElligott and K. Redmond (1954–55)	£12	£40
J. J. McElligott and T. K. Whitaker (1957–60)	£10	£25
M. Ó Muimhneacháin and T. K. Whitaker (1962–68)	£10	£20
T. K. Whitaker and C. H. Murray (1969–70)	£10	£20
T. K. Whitaker and C. H. Murray (1971–75)	£5	£10
C. H. Murray and M. O. Murchú (1976)	£5	£10

FIVE POUNDS

1943–75 ISSUE

Brown on yellow and mauve underprint. 166 x 92mm
Signatures:

Joseph Brennan and J. J. McElligott (1943–44)	£80	£150
Joseph Brennan and J. J. McElligott (1945–51)	£45	£70
Joseph Brennan and J. J. McElligott (1952–53)	£20	£35
J. J. McElligott and K. Redmond (1954–55)	£25	£70
J. J. McElligott and T. K. Whitaker (1957–60)	£20	£35
M. Ó Muimhneacháin and T. K. Whitaker (1961–68)	£20	£35
T. K. Whitaker and C. H. Murray (1969–70)	£20	£35
T. K. Whitaker and C. H. Murray (1971–75)	£14	£25

Series A, "Lady Lavery". Central Bank of Ireland (continued)   *VF*   *EF*

TEN POUNDS

1943–60 ISSUE

Blue on green and mauve underprint. 189 x 107mm
Signatures:

	VF	EF
Joseph Brennan and J. J. McElligott (1943–44)	£150	£200
Joseph Brennan and J. J. McElligott (1945–52)	£40	£75
J. J. McElligott and K. Redmond (1954–55)	£75	£100
J. J. McElligott and T. K. Whitaker (1957–1960)	£40	£75

TWENTY POUNDS

1943–76 ISSUE

Red on orange and mauve underprint. 203 x 114mm
Signatures:

	VF	EF
Joseph Brennan and J. J. McElligott (1943–44)	£650	£850
Joseph Brennan and J. J. McElligott (1945–52)	£175	£300
J. J. McElligott and K. Redmond (1954–55)	£165	£300
J. J. McElligott and T. K. Whitaker (1957)	£150	£300
M. Ó Muimhneacháin and T. K. Whitaker (1961–65)	£80	£250
T. K. Whitaker and C. H. Murray (1969–75)	£40	£100
T. K. Whitaker and M. O. Murchú (1976)	£40	£100

FIFTY POUNDS

1943–77 ISSUE

Mauve on yellow underprint. 203 x 114mm
Signatures:

	VF	EF
Joseph Brennan and J. J. McElligott (1943–51)	£300	£500
J. J. McElligott and K. Redmond (1954–55)	£300	£500
J. J. McElligott and T. K. Whitaker (1957–60)	£180	£400
M. Ó Muimhneacháin and T. K. Whitaker (1962–68)	£180	£300
T. K. Whitaker and C. H. Murray (1970–75)	£130	£250
C. H. Murray and M. O. Murchú (1977)	£90	£175

ONE HUNDRED POUNDS

1943–76 ISSUE

Black on yellow and mauve underprint. 203 x 114mm
Signatures:

	VF	EF
Joseph Brennan and J. J. McElligott (1943–49)	£300	£500
J. J. McElligott and K. Redmond (1954)	£200	£550
J. J. McElligott and T. K. Whitaker (1959)	£180	£475
M. Ó Muimhneacháin and T. K. Whitaker (1963–68)	£180	£375
T. K. Whitaker and C. H. Murray (1970–75)	£130	£375
C. H. Murray and M. O. Murchú (1977)	£130	£300

For a concise and complete study of the notes of Ireland
visit the website
www.irishpapermoney.com

CENTRAL BANK OF IRELAND
SERIES B NOTES, 1976–93

ONE POUND

1976–93 ISSUE

Green on multicoloured underprint. 151 x 84mm
Signatures:

	EF	UNC
C. H. Murray and M. O. Murchú (1977)	£5	£10
C. H. Murray and Tomás F. Ó Cofaigh (1978–81)	£5	£10
Tomás F. Ó Cofaigh and Maurice F. Doyle (1982–87)	£5	£10
Maurice F. Doyle and S. P. Cromien (1988–89)	£3	£8

FIVE POUNDS

1976–93 ISSUE

Brown on multicoloured underprint. 156 x 83mm
Signatures:

	EF	UNC
T. K. Whitaker and C. H. Murray (1976)	£15	£25
C. H. Murray and M. O Murchú (1976–77)	£10	£20
C. H. Murray and Tomás F. Ó Cofaigh (1979–81)	£10	£22
Tomás F. Ó Cofaigh and Maurice F. Doyle (1983–87)	£10	£20
Maurice F. Doyle and S. P. Cromien (1988–93)	£8	£20

Central Bank of Ireland. Series B (continued)   *EF*   *UNC*

TEN POUNDS

1976–93 ISSUE
Purple on multicoloured underprint. 164 x 86mm
Signatures:

	EF	UNC
C. H. Murray and Tomás F. Ó Cofaigh (1978–81)	£22	£38
Tomás F. Ó Cofaigh and Maurice F. Doyle (1983–87)	£20	£35
Maurice F. Doyle and S. P. Cromien (1987–93)	£16	£35

TWENTY POUNDS

1976–93 ISSUE
Blue on multicoloured underprint. 172 x 90mm
Signatures:

	EF	UNC
C. H. Murray and Tomás F. Ó Cofaigh (1980–81)	£35	£45
Tomás F. Ó Cofaigh and Maurice F. Doyle (1983–86)	£35	£45
Maurice F. Doyle and S. P. Cromien (1988–89)	£32	£45

FIFTY POUNDS

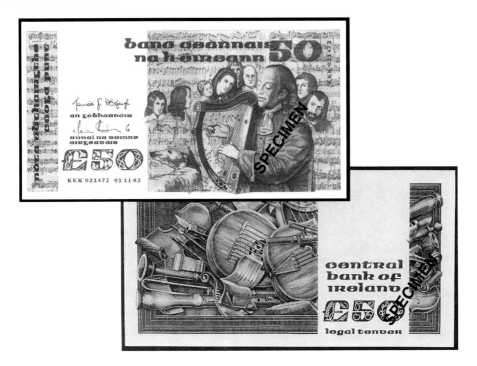

1976–93 ISSUE

Brown on multicoloured underprint. 180 x 94mm
Signatures:
Tomás F. Ó Cofaigh and Maurice F. Doyle (1982) £85   £120
Maurice F. Doyle and S. P. Cromien (1991) £70   £100

EF   UNC

CENTRAL BANK OF IRELAND
SERIES C NOTES, 1992–2001

FIVE POUNDS

1992–2001 ISSUE
Brown and blue on multicoloured underprint. 120 x 64mm
Signatures:
Maurice F. Doyle and S. P. Cromien (1994) .... — £12●
Muiris S. Ó Conaill and P. Mullarkey (Dec. 1994–97) .... — £12●
Muiris S. Ó Conaill and P. Mullarkey (Dec. 1998) .... — £15

TEN POUNDS

1992–2001 ISSUE
Brown, blue and green on multicoloured underprint. 128 x 68mm
Signatures:
Maurice F. Doyle and S. P. Cromien (1993–94) .... — £15●
Muiris S. Ó Conaill and P. Mullarkey (1995–97) .... — £15●
Muiris S. Ó Conaill and P. Mullarkey (Dec. 1997–98) .... — £14

Central Bank of Ireland. Series C (continued)   *EF*   *UNC*

TWENTY POUNDS

1992–2001 ISSUE
Mauve and brown on multicoloured underprint. 136 x 72mm
Signatures:

Maurice F. Doyle and S. P. Cromien (1992–94)	—	£35
Muiris S. Ó Conaill and P. Mullarkey (1995–97)	—	£30
Muiris S. Ó Conaill and P. Mullarkey (1997–98)	—	£30

FIFTY POUNDS

1992–2001 ISSUE
Blue and green on multicoloured underprint. 144 x 76mm
Signatures:

Muiris S. Ó Conaill and P. Mullarkey (1995–96) ....   —   £100

ONE HUNDRED POUNDS

1992–2001 ISSUE
Purple, red and blue on multicoloured underprint. 152 x 80mm
Signatures:

Muiris S. Ó Conaill and P. Mullarkey (1996) ....   —   £200

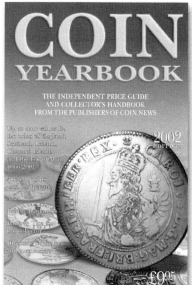

COIN YEARBOOK 2002

STILL ONLY £9.95

The 2002 Edition of the acclaimed COIN YEARBOOK—*Order yours today!*

Published in November 2001, the COIN YEARBOOK 2002 is promising to be our very best edition yet with exiting new features, additional illustrations and up-to-the minute pricing—all vital reading whether you are the seasoned professional or keen amateur. Totally INDEPENDENT this is the only price guide and collector's handbook you will ever need. Published by those in the hobby, for the hobby. Fully revised for the coming year with accurate valuations on English, Scottish, Irish and Channel Island Coins printed on blue pages for easier reference.

As well as the price guide there are useful sections not found in any similar publication including: Coin Collector's Review of the Past Year; Comprehensive Guide to the latest auction Prices; a guide to mint marks and denominations of the world; Plus useful information on every aspect of coin collecting from the legal implications of a coin found by metal detector to how to care your collection.

Plus, as in the past there will be the updated index to COIN NEWS so that you can look up those informative articles in your magazine using this simple contents guide.

To be sure of your copy (don't forget, the last edition sold out by July 12) order your copy today using the form below.

The International Bank Note Society

Founded in 1961 as a non-profit making society, The International Bank Note Society (IBNS) aims to encourage collectors of paper money and to provide them with an organisation in which they can get to know one another.

With regular meetings, newsletters and a quarterly journal, the society helps collectors to keep abreast of recent developments and initiatives.

Mail bid auctions are also held as are congresses in both the UK and overseas.

For further information on how to join *the* Society for paper money collectors contact:

Laurence Pope
2 Tattershall Drive,
Market Deeping,
Peterborough, PE6 8BS.

Bank of England

A Specimen note of the Wartime 10 shilling.

...nk of England note for one hundred pounds dated 1790 and bearing the handwritten serial number 19...
...note is signed by R. Sambrook and J. Pretty on behalf of Abraham Newland the Chief Cashier at the tim...
...note is one of the earliest known and was sold by Spink at their auction on October 6, 2000. For its ag...

During the 19th century in Great Britain many cities, towns and even villages had banks which issued their
own notes. These are known as "Provincial" notes and are eagerly sought after, especially by local historians.
The notes illustrated above were all sold by Spink in their auction on October 6 and illustrated with their kind

Guernsey

Jersey

Isle of Man

Scotland

Ireland

A selection of world notes

World notes come in a variety of shapes, sizes and designs giving the collector a wealth of material to choose from. The notes illustrated here were taken from Spink's catalogue of their auction of October 5, 2001 or from the list of John Pettit Pty, Ltd.

Unusual notes to look out for

During World War II English notes on the island of Guernsey were withdrawn and overprinted by the Germans—these notes are much sought after today (illustration courtesy of John Pettit).

During the American Civil war both sides produced a plethora of notes. Those of the Confederate States are particularly attractive and avaidly collected today. The newcomer is warned to be on guard as there are many counterfeits and forgeries of these issues.

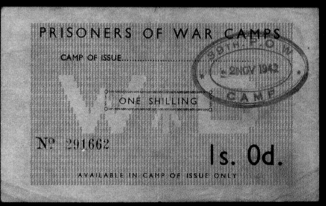

In times of war or other emergencies many different notes are produced including special notes for use in prisoner of war camps. These, including this note produced for the British War Department and used at Castle Camp, Maxstoke during World War II, are extremely collectable (illustration courtesy of John Pettit).

The Government of Antigua and Barbuda authorised an edition of notes to be produced on gold leaf—although attractive they never really gained the approval of collectors.

Notgeld (see Glossary on page 30) comes in many different forms including these colourful issues. They were produced in Germany after World War I.

Dr Willem F. Duisenberg, President of the European Central Bank, launches the new euro notes at an event in Frankfurt in August 2001.

Here comes . . . .
THE EURO

ON AUGUST 30, 2001, little more than a hundred days before the introduction of the euro coins and banknotes, Dr Willem F. Duisenberg, President of the European Central Bank (ECB), unveiled the forthcoming notes and their security features. The seven euro banknotes now being produced to the highest international security standards, incorporate a very large number of security features, combining existing features in the national currencies of the euro area, with a number of new features which have been specifically designed for the euro banknotes. Three simple tests—feel, look and tilt— will enable the public and cash handlers to identify genuine notes quickly and easily. In order to inform citizens of the forthcoming banknotes, the ECB and the twelve national central banks of the euro area are launching a massive media campaign under the slogan "THE EURO, OUR MONEY", including posters, television, the cinema, newspaper features and advertising and household delivery of leaflets and brochures.

While the controversy continues to rage in Britain over whether or when we should abandon our sterling currency and fall into line with our European partners, 12 of the 15 EU countries are now poised to scrap their punts, lire, francs, deutschemarks and kroner, and replace them with the euro on January 1, 2002.

This is the culmination of a campaign which has been going for more than a decade. It began in 1991 when the European Council of Ministers agreed to adopt a currency union by 1999. The following year member countries ratified the Maastricht Treaty, although Britain only did so with great reservations. By 1995 the European Union abandoned the original name of European Currency Unit (ECU). This had been particularly favoured by the French, largely because it reminded them of the glorious reign of Louis XIV when the Ecu (shield) was the most popular coin of its day.

Other alternatives which were briefly suggested and just as rapidly dropped were eurodollar and euromark. Instead, the term Euro was agreed as being the least likely to offend national sentiment among the member countries. Having decided on a name, the next step was to design a symbol for it. More than 30 designs were submitted to the European Council, and these were whittled down to ten which were thrown open to public debate. The final choice, however, was left to Jacques Santer, then President of the EU Commission, and Yves-Thibault de Silguy, commissioner in charge of the new currency. The winning motif is based on the lower-case Greek letter epsilon which is the initial letter of the word "Europe". The twin horizontal lines are intended to symbolise the euro's stability, although vertical or horizontal strokes are traditionally used in letters denoting forms of currency, such as the pound, lira, yen or dollar.

At the same time, the start date was put back three years to give participating countries more time to adjust to the new system which entailed changing vending machines and banking systems. In 1999, when the euro should have come into use, the European Union published the designs for the standard reverses of the coins and the motifs of the notes to be released by the European Central Bank, headquartered at Frankfurt am Main in Germany.

While the coins have identical weights and specifications, as well as standard motifs on the reverse, to appease national sentiment each country will have its own distinctive motifs on the obverse. The standard reverses of the eight coins from 1 cent to 2 euro were designed by Luc Luycx of Belgium, winner of an international design competition which was held between February and September 1996, and consisted of three motifs essentially featuring a map of western Europe with the numerals of value, for the three bronze, three brass and two bimetallic coins. The distinctive obverses are an interesting mixture of royal portraiture, symbolism and pictorialism. While several countries have opted for a uniform obverse, Germany is using a sprig of oak on the three lowest denominations (analogous to the motif on the reverse of the

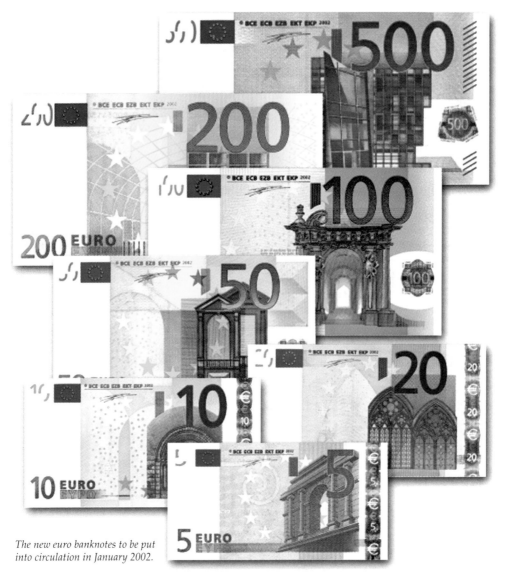

The new euro banknotes to be put into circulation in January 2002.

pfennig coins), with the Brandenburg Gate on the middle values and the German eagle on the two euro values. Both Austria and Italy have gone for a different motif on each coin, famous Austrians and Italian works of art respectively, while Greece (the most recent country to sign up) has a mixture of shipping and a portrait of the great patriot Eleftherios Venizelos on the cents and an Athenian 'owl' tetradrachm of the 4th century BC and Europa and the Bull on the two euro coins.

The designs for the seven notes (5, 10, 20, 50, 100, 200 and 500 euro) to be issued by the European Central Bank were produced by the Austrian graphic artist, Robert Kalina, who submitted them for the approval of the Council of Europe meeting at Dublin in December 1996. The front of each note features windows in different architectural styles, from the classical to the ultra-modern, while the backs have a map of Europe on the right, the European flag on the left and different styles of bridges through the ages from a Roman viaduct (5 euro) to the Pont de Neuilly in Paris (100e) and the Normandie Bridge (500e).

The word EURO and the Greek equivalent appear alongside the figures in the bottom left-hand corner of both sides, but the only other inscription is the set of initials BCE, ECB, EZB, EKT and EKP representing the name of the Bank in the various languages of the EU (and in case you are wondering EKT is actually the Greek initials of *Evropaike*

Kentrike Trapeza). Below these initials appear the distinguished if illegible signature of the Bank President.

Production of the notes has been shared by the security printers of several countries. The Banque de France printing works at Chamalières has had serious technical problems in getting its quota of 2.5 billion notes ready in time for release at the end of 2001. And even if the French authorities take delivery of the notes in time, and get them into the banks and the shops, this is only half the problem, for there is also the headache of recalling obsolete francs over the ensuing six months. Traditionally, many French people have distrusted banks, and preferred to hoard their cash under the mattress or in a hole in the wall. There is also the potentially embarrassing matter of turning in vast quantities of notes and having the unwelcome attention of the French equivalent of the Inland Revenue asking awkward questions. In a move to combat money laundering banks are required to notify the fiscal authorities if deposits of more than 50,000 francs are made. The Banque de France has already published statistics which reveal that three quarters of all 500 franc notes (the highest denomination now current) cannot be accounted for at the present time, while a fifth of all 200 franc notes issued since 1960 have unaccountably vanished from the scene. A staggering 150 billion francs were estimated to be lying around, and the conversion to the euro seems likely to create an enormous windfall for the tax authorites. It is believed that the problem may be almost as great in Italy.

In May 2000 the 12 countries—Austria, Belgium, Finland, France, Germany, Greece, Ireland, Italy, Luxembourg, Netherlands, Portugal and Spain—began tentatively introducing the euro into everyday life. Shops were encouraged to display prices in dual currency, and on May 9 that year the annual Europa stamps appeared in euros as well as the respective national currencies. On previous occasions each participating country had produced its own motifs, though in a common theme, but on this occasion the majority opted for a design by Jean-Paul Cousin of France showing a tower of five-pointed stars. Since September 2000 the concept of dual-currency stamps has been considerably extended, both definitive and special issues being inscribed in euro cents as well as the indigenous currencies. From January 1, 2002, however, stamps will only be denominated in euro although there will be a six-month period in which stamps in the obsolete national currencies will still be valid for postage.

Germany led the way in converting postage meters to the new currency and since the beginning of 2001 meter marks have often been inscribed solely in euro cents. There has also been a nationwide campaign of slogan postmarks to remind the public that the euro was coming.

Several countries have issued stamps to publicise the changeover. As far back as 1998 Italy issued a stamp showing the cogwheels of machinery embellished with the euro symbol and the reverses of the Italian euro coins, while the euro symbol was a recurring motif on the stamps released later the same year to publicise the Italia '98 stamp show.

Ireland contributed a 30p/38 cent stamp and the Netherlands an 80 cent stamp, both showing the reverse of the bimetallic euro coin. Another version of the euro coin can also be found on a recent stamp from Greece celebrating the centenary of the Post Office Savings Bank.

So far, however, Germany is the only country to issue a stamp showing the banknotes. In 1998 the inauguration of the European Central Bank was celebrated by a stamp showing the initials EZB made up of a montage of the banknotes, with the twelve European stars superimposed.

As E-day drew closer, the propaganda accelerated within the EU countries that had signed up for the single currency, culminating in the distribution of explanatory brochures to all 200 million households in the dozen countries. At the same time, teaching packs for schools and various games and competitions for children have been widely disseminated, while advertising in newspapers, radio and television has also been stepped up.

Apart from the ephemera associated with the greatest monetary revolution since the Roman Empire, it is anticipated that there will be considerable numbers of collectables, in the form of sets of obsolete coins and banknotes linked to the new currency, philanumismatic covers and banknote folders. Clearly, an exciting time lies ahead.

An example of the reverses of the notes. The 5 euros.

Left: The Bank of England as "The Old Lady" here in a satirical cartoon from Punch.
Above: Bust of William Paterson who originally proposed the establishment of the Bank of England in 1694.

Images from the Bank of England Museum's recent exhibition "Forgery: The Artful Crime".

Right: A coloured engraving, 1818 showing an unfortunate being dragged before the Bank's directors accused of an offence in connection with a forged banknote. The bank men are, however, unable to confirm that the note in question is a forgery.
Below: An inking knife, forged plate, paper bearing off-set notes and other forger's tools.

The Bank of England Museum

THE BANK OF ENGLAND was founded in 1694 by Royal Charter which was granted by virtue of an Act of Parliament based on the proposals of a Scotsman, William Paterson from Dumfries. The Act provided that subscribers to the capital of £1,200,000 should be incorporated as the Governor and Company of the Bank of England. It was granted certain privileges on condition that the entire capital should be lent at 8 per cent to the government which was then strapped for cash in its war with France.

Initially the business of the Bank was conducted at Mercers' Hall but at the end of 1694 it moved to Grocers' Hall where it remained until 1734. A decade earlier, however, the Bank acquired a site in Threadneedle Street. George Sampson erected the original Bank building between 1732 and 1734 and on June 5 in the latter year the Bank took possession of its new premises. Between 1765 and 1788 wings were added to the original structure by Sir Robert Taylor, entailing the demolition of the Church of St Christopher-le-Stocks in 1781. The rest of the four-acre site was acquired in the course of the 18th century and the buildings on the north side were erected from designs by Sir John Soane who was the Bank's architect from 1788 till 1833. Soane also rebuilt or remodelled the work of his predecessors, but the Court Room, erected by Taylor in 1767 and decorated in the Adam style, was retained unaltered until the Bank was substantially rebuilt in the period after World War I.

The prodigious increase in the Bank's operations during and immediately after that war rendered the existing buildings inadequate. While the outer walls were retained, the interior of the Bank was completely rebuilt between 1925 and 1937 to designs by Sir Herbert Baker which retained the high-domed chambers of Soane's project and even managed to incorporate many of the original decorative features. Thus the Baroque character of the old buildings has been beautifully preserved in "the Old Lady

of Threadneedle Street". The pediment of the building has a relatively modern representation of Britannia sculpted by Charles Wheeler, and below this are six buttress figures representing bearers and guardians of wealth.

The massive bronze doors of the Bank are replete with symbolism. Latin inscriptions on the central doors, placed around the heads of lions, record the dates of the Bank's foundation and rebuilding. There are pictorial motifs which contrast the modes of communication in 1694 and the 20th century, as well as the hand of Zeus grasping a lightning bolt (symbolising electricity) and lions guarding piles of money, symbolism borrowed from the Mycenean era.

Although the Bank of England was a private company, over the 300 years since its foundation it has gradually assumed the functions of a state bank. It is the banker to the government and has the management of all government stocks as regards transfers and the payment of dividends, and it is the sole note-issuing bank in England and Wales. Most important of all, it is the bankers' bank and as a result it is the ultimate cash repository of the country.

A major tourist attraction is the Museum housed within the Bank of England which traces the history of banking in this country with specific reference to the Bank, from its modest beginning in 1694 to its present status as the nation's central bank.

There are gold bars dating from ancient times to the modern market bar, a prodigious

Sir Herbert Baker's Rotunda in the museum.

One of the Museum's many fascinating displays.

The museum boasts the latest technology.

collection of coins and a unique collection of banknotes dating back more than 300 years, as well as many other items which one might not, at first glance, associate with a bank. Here, for example, you will find pikes, muskets and other military equipment associated with the Bank's defence. This dates back to 1780 when the Bank's security was threatened during the Gordon Riots. From then onwards an officer and 24 other ranks from one of the Guards regiments carried out guard duty over the premises each night.

There is also a fascinating display of Roman pottery and the mosaics which were excavated in 1930 during the rebuilding process. Documents relating to famous customers, such as the Duchess of Marlborough, George Washington and Horatio Nelson, are also on show. As a government institution, inevitably the Bank has had its share of criticism over the centuries and some of the scurrilous lampoons and cartoons satirising the Bank in prints, engravings and newspapers reflect this.

By contrast, the latest interactive technology lets you explore the bank and its history, monitor the stock exchange live, or try your hand as a dealer in foreign exchange. You can examine the intricacies of banknote design and production and begin to appreciate the extraordinary lengths taken as a precaution against forgery.

So come behind the doors of the Old Lady of Threadneedle Street and learn more about what everyone's bank does for you. Oh, and by the way, entrance is free, so you don't have to break in.

Bank of England Museum
Threadneedle Street
London EC2 8AH

Telephone: 0207 601 5545
E-mail: museum@bankofengland.co.uk
Website: www.bankofengland.co.uk

The nearest Underground to the museum is Bank.
Opening times: Monday-Friday, 10am-5pm throughout the year.
Closed: weekends and public holidays. Admission free.
Special presentations for booked groups. Access for the disabled.

Books
for the banknote collector

On the following pages is a list of books of interest to the banknote collector. They are listed under their area of main interest and by author alphabetically. Many of the titles are out of print but can often be acquired from your favourite numismatic bookseller.

General

IAN ANGUS, *Paper Money*, London, 1974.
COURTNEY L. COLLING Guide & checklist of World Notgeld 1914–1947, 2000.
JOE CRIBB, *Money: From Cowrie Shells to Credit Cards*, London 1986.
LESLIE DUNKLING and ADRIAN ROOM, *The Guinness Book of Money*, Enfield, 1990.
W. KRANISTER, *The Moneymakers International*, Cambridge, 1989.
BARRY KRAUSE, *Collecting Paper Money for Pleasure and Profit.*
MONETARY RESEARCH INSTITUTE *Bankers Guide to Foreign currency*, Housten TX, 2001.
COLIN NARBETH, ROBIN HENDY AND CHRISTOPHER STOCKER, *Collecting Paper Money and Bonds*, London, 1979.
COLIN NARBETH, *Encyclopedia of Paper Money*, London, 1967.
JOHN ORNA-ORNSTEIN, *The Story of Money*, London, 1997.
ALBERT PICK, *Briefmarkengeld*, Brunswick, 1970.
Papiergeld, Brunswick, 1967.
Papiergeldkatalog Europa seit 1900, Munich, 1973. *Paper Money Catalogue of the Americas*, Munich, 1973.
Standard Catalog of World Paper Money, 3 vols., Krause Publications, Iola, 1998.
FRED REINFELD, *The Story of Paper Money.*
JOHN E. SANDROCK, *World Paper Money Collection*, New York, various editions.
FRED SCHWANN, *Collecting Paper Money*, New York, 1996.
NEIL SHAFER, *The Wonderful World of Paper Money*, 1972.
Let's Collect Paper Money, 1976.
GEORGE J. STEN, *Banknotes of the World*, 2 vols, Menlo Park, 1967.
Encyclopedia of World Paper Money, New York, 1965.

Military Invasion and Occupation Notes

JAMES MACKAY, *Banknotes at War*, London, 1977.
CARLTON F. SCHWAN, *Military Payment Certificates World War II Allied Military Currency*, Ohio, 1974.
CARLTON F. SCWHAN AND JOSEPH E. BOLING, *World War II Military Currency*, Ohio, 1978.
JAMES RUTLANDER, *Allied Military Currency*, New York, 1968.
NEIL SHAFER, *Philippine Emergency and Guerrilla Currency of World War II*, Racine, 1974.
ARLIE SLABAUGH, *Japanese Invasion Money*, Chicago, 1977.

GASTONE SOLLNER, *Moneta d'Occupazione e di Liberazione della IIa Guerra Mondiale*, Mantua, 1965
ZVI STAHL, *Jewish Ghettos' and Concentration Camps' Money (1933-45)*, Israel, 1990.
RAYMOND TOY, *World War II Allied Military Currency*, San Diego, 1969.
RAYMOND TOY AND BOB MEYER, *World War II Axis Military Currency*, Tucson, 1967.
BENJAMIN WHITE, *The Currency of the Great War*, London, 1921.
JOHN F. YARWOOD, *A Guide to British Military Tokens*, Horsham, Australia, 1998.

Algeria

PAUL DUGENDRE, *Catalogue des Billets de la Banque de l'Algerie et de la Tunisie*, Paris, 1953.

Angola

LUIS M.R. DE SOUSA, *O Papel-Moeda em Angola*, Luanda, 1969.

Argentina

JOSE MARIA MUNARI, *Papel Moneda Argentina 1935-1967*, Buenos Aires, 1967.

Australia

GREG MCDONALD, *Australian Coins and Banknotes*, Umina Beach, 1985.
ALAN NICHOLSON, *Australian Banknote Catalogue*, Melbourne, 1979.
DION H. SKINNER, *Rennick's Australian Coins and Banknotes Guide*, Adelaide, 1980.
P. STEELE, *Collect Australian Coins and Banknotes*, Dubbo NSW, 1988.
G.W. TOMLINSON, *Australian Bank Notes 1817–1963*, Melbourne, 1963.
MICHAEL VORT-RONALD, *Collect Australian Banknotes*, Dubbo NSW, 1998.

Austria

ALBERT PICK AND R. RICHTER, *Oesterreich Banknoten und Staatspapiergeld ab 1759*, Berlin, 1972.

Baltic States

A. PLATBARZDIS, *Coins and Notes of Estonia, Latvia, Lithuania*, Stockholm, 1968.
M. TITUS, *Paper Currencies of Estonia*, Menlo Park, 1971.

Belgium

J. DE MEY, *Le Papier-Monnaie Belge d'Outremer, 1896-1963*, Brussels, 1976. *Le Papier-Monnaie Belge, 1814–1976*, Brussels, 1976.

IBNS, *Paper Money of the 20th Century: Belgium and Colonies*, St. Louis, 1975.

FRANCOIS MORIN, *Catalogue des Billets de Banque Belge 1900 a 1974*, Brussels, 1974. *Cataloge des Billets de Banque de Congo* etc, Boom, 1974.

Bolivia

LUIS A. ASBUN-KARMY, *Monedas de Bolivia*, La Paz, 1977.

Brazil

BANCO DO BRASIL, *Cedulas Brasileiras*, Rio de Janeiro, 1965.

ALVARO GONCALVES, *Catalogo de Cedulas e Moedas Brasileiras*, Sao Paulo, 1969.

DALE A. SEPPA, *The Paper Money of Brazil*, Chicago, 1976.

VIOLO LISSA, *Catalogo do Papel-Moeda do Brasil*, Brasilia, 1981.

DOS SANTOS TRINGUEIROS, *Dinhero do Brasil*, Rio de Janeiro, 1966.

A. TODISCO, *Catalogue of Brazilian Banknotes*, IBNS, 1961.

British West Africa

RICHARD J. FORD, *British West African Currency Board Bank Notes*, Walton-on-the-Naze, 1970.

Burma

M. ROBINSON AND L.A. SHAW, *The Coins and Banknotes of Burma*, Manchester, 1980.

Canada

BANK OF CANADA, *The Story of Canada's Currency*, Ottawa, 1981. *The National Currency Collection and the Bank of Canada Currency Museum*, n.d.

J.E. CHARLTON, *Standard Catalogue of Canadian Paper Money*, Toronto, 1980.

HANS ZOELL, *Simplified Catalog of Canadian-Newfoundland Coins and Paper Money*, 1961.

Chile

JOSE M. GALETOVIC AND HECTOR BENAVIDES, *El Billete Chileno*, Santiago, 1973.

China

W.H. LU, *Paper Money Catalogue of the People's Republic of China and Macau*, Kuala Lumpur, 1998.

KING-ON MAO, *History of Chinese Paper Currency*, Hong Kong, 1968-77. *History of Paper Currency of the People's Republic of China*, Hong Kong, 1972.

WARD D. SMITH AND BRIAN MATRAVERS, *Chinese Banknotes*, Menlo Park, USA, 1970.

HSU YIH TZON, *The Illustrated Encyclopedia of the Chinese Banknotes*, Taipei, 1981.

Colombia

YASHA BERESINER AND EDOUARDO DARGENT, *Catalogue of the Paper Money of Colombia and Peru*, London 1973.

ERNESTO CALLEJOS, *Catalogo de Billetes Emitidos...de Colombia*, Medellin, 1978.

Cuba

NEIL SHAFER, *Cuban Paper Money 1857-1968*, St. Louis, 1970.

Cyprus

MAJOR F. PRIDMORE, *Modern Coins and Notes of Cyprus*, London, 1974.

Denmark

AXEL RUBOW, *Nationalbankens Historie 1878-1908*, Copenhagen, 1920.

FROVIN SIEG, *Seddelkatalog 1874-1976*, Ulbjerg, 1977.

El Salvador

ALCEDO F. ALMANZAR AND BRIAN R. STICKNEY, *The Coins and Paper Money of El Salvador*, San Antonio, 1973.

ENRIQUE FRANKE, *The Banknotes of the Republic of El Salvador*, San Salvador, 1974.

England

W. MARSTON ACRES, *The Bank of England from Within*, Oxford, 1931.

DAVID BEVAN, *A Guide to Collecting English Banknotes*, New Malden, 1970.

BRYAN BURKE, *Nazi Counterfeiting of British Currency in World War II*, San Bernardino, 198.7

G. CHANDLER, *Four Centuries of Banking*, 2 vols, 1964–68.

SIR JOHN CLAPHAM, *The Bank of England: A History*, Cambridge, 1944.

W. CRICK AND J. WADSWORTH, *A Hundred Years of Joint-Stock Banking*, London, 1958.

VINCENT DUGGLEBY, *English Paper Money*, London, 1990.

PHILIP GEDDES, *Inside the Bank of England*, London, 1987.

G.L. GRANT, *Standard Catalogue of Provincial Banks and Banknotes*, London, 1977.

T. GREGORY, *The Westminster Bank Through a Century*, London, 1936.

VIRGINIA HEWITT AND J.M. KEYWORTH, *As Good as Gold*, London, 1987.

C.R. JOSSET, *Money in Britain*, Newton Abbott, 1971.

JAMES MACBURNIE, *The Story of the Yorkshire and Lancashire Bank*, Manchester, 1922.

A.D. MACKENZIE, *The Bank of England Note*, Cambridge, 1953.

P.W. MATTHEWS AND A.W. TUKE, *The History of Barclays Bank*, London, 1926.

DAVID M. MILLER, *Bank of England and Treasury Notes 1694-1970*, Newcastle, 1970.

COLIN NARBETH, *Collect British Banknotes*, London, 1970.

R.S. SAYERS, *The Bank of England, 1891-1944*, Cambridge, 1976.

H. WITHERS, *National Provincial Bank, 1833-1933*, London, 1933.

Finland

ERKKI BORG, *Suomessa Kaytetet Raha*t, Helsinki, 1976.

FINLANDS BANK, *Inhemska Sedeltyper in Finland, 1809-1951*, Helsinki, 1952.

HANNU PAATELA, *Research Collection of Bank Notes Used in Finland 1662-1978*, Helsinki, 1978.

KURT PETTERSON, *Suomen Rahojen Hinnasta 1811-1979*, Helsinki., 1979.

TUKKO TOLVIO, *The Coins and Banknotes of Finland*.

France

JEAN LAFAURIE AND RAYMOND HABREKORN, *Catalogue des Emissions Officielles Francaises de Papier-Monnaie 1797-1952*, Auxerre, 1953-4.

M. MUSZYNSKI, *Les Billets de la Banque de France*, Villiers sur Marne, 1975 .

ARGUS THIMONIER, *Monnaies et Billets Francxe depuis 1774*, Paris, 1960.

Germany

KURT JAEGER AND ULLRICH HAEVECKER, *Die Deutschen Banknoten seit 1871*, Cologne, 1979.

ARNOLD KELLER. *Das Papiergeld des Ersten Weltkrieges*, Berlin, 1957.
Das Papiergeld des Zweiten Weltkrieges, Berlin, 1953.
Das Papiergeld der Deutschen Kolonien, Munster, 1967.

KAI LINDMAN, *serienscheine*, Sassenburg, 2000.

MANFRED MULLER AND ANTON GEIGER, *Das papiergeld der Deutschen Eisenbahnen und der Reichspost*, Frankenthal, 2000

ALBERT PICK AND J. RIXEN, *Papiergeld Spezialkatalog Deutschland 1874-1980*, Berlin, 1982.

Gibraltar

D.C. DEVENISH, *Currency Notes of Gibraltar*, London, 1969.

Greece

PAUL G. PYLARINOS, *Greek Paper Money*, Athens, 1976.

A. TARASSOULEAS, *Paper Money of Greece*, Athens, 1982.

Greenland

PETER FLENSBORG, *Gronlandske Pengesedler, 1803-1967*, Copenhagen, 1970.

Guatemala

ODIS H. CLARK, *Paper Money of Guatemala, 1834-1946*, San Antonio, 1971.

DWIGHTR MUSSER, *The Paper Money of Guatemala*, USA, 1959.

Hawaii

MAURICE M. GOULD AND KEWNNETH BRESSETT, *Hawaiian Coins, Tokens and Paper Money*, Racine, 1961.

GORDON MEDCALF AND ROBERT FONG, *Hawaiian Money and Medals*, Kailua, 1967.
Paper Money of the Kingdom of Hawaii 1859-1905, Honolulu, 1966.
AND RONALD RUSSELL, Hawaiian Money Standard Catalog, Honolulu., 1978.

Hungary

RICHARD A. BANYAI, *The Legal and Monetary Aspects of the Hungarian Hyper-inflation*, Tucson, 1971.

MIHALY KUPA AND BELA AMBRUS, *Magyarorszag Papirpenzei*, Budapest, 1964. *Paper Money of Hungary 1803-1918*, Budapest, 1963.

Iceland

FINNUR KOLBEINSSON, *Islenzkar Myntir*, Reykjavik, 1978.

India

KISHORE JHUNJHUNWALA, *Indian Paper Money Since 1950*, Mumbai, 1998.

Indonesia

DONALD L. FOLTZ, *Paper Money of the Republic of Indonesia*, Indianapolis, 1970.

Ireland

G. BARROW, *The Emergence of the Irish Banking System*, Dublin, 1975.

MARTAN MAC DEVITT, *Irish Banknotes, Irish Government Paper Money from 1928*, Dublin, 1999.

DEREK YOUNG, *Guide to the Currency of Ireland, Legal tender Notes 1928-1972*, Dublin, 1972.
Guide to the Currency of Ireland, Consolidated Bank Notes, 1929-1941, Dublin, 1977.

Isle of Man

ISLE OF MAN BANK, *100 Years of Banking*, Douglas, 1965.

ERNEST QUARMBY, *Banknotes & Banking in the Isle of Man 1788-1970*, London, 1971.

PILCHER RALFE, *Sixty Years of Banking, 1865-1925*, Douglas, 1926.

Israel

SYLVIA HAFFNER, *The History of Modern Israel's Money from 1917-1967*, San Diego, 1968.

A.H. KAHAN, *Israel's Money and Medals*, New York, 1976.

Italy

CESARE BOBBA, *Carta Moneta Italiane, Asti*, 1974.
Catalogo della Carta-Moneta d'Occupazione, Asti, 1975.

MARIO DE FANTI, *Carta-Moneta Italiana, 1866-1961*, Casciano, 1966 .

LUIGI DE ROSA, *Il Banco di Napoli Istituto di Emissione*, Naples, 1976.

LIBERO MANCINI, *Catalogo Italiano della Cartamoneta 1746-1966*, Bologna, 1966.

ADOLFO MINI, *La Carta Moneta italiana 1746-1960*, Palermo, 1967.

GASTONE SOLLNER, *Catalogo della Carta-Moneta Italiana dal 1866 ad Oggi*, Milan, 1964.

Jamaica

JEROME REMICK, *Jamaican Banknotes*, St. Louis, 1968.

Japan

BANKOKU KAHEI KENKYUKAI, *Government and Bank of Japan Issues and Military Issues*, Tokyo, 1970.

IBNS, *Paper Money of the 20th Century: Japan*, St. Louis, 1981.

Y. OHASHI, *Nippon Shihei Taikei Zukan*, Tokyo, 1957.

Katanga

PETER SYMES, *The Bank Notes of Katanga*, Kirkcaldy, 1998.

Korea

BANK OF KOREA, *The History of Korean Money*, Seoul, 1969.

KIM IN SIK, *Illustrated Catalog of Korean Currency*, Seoul, 1978.

Luxembourg

FERN WICTOR, *Monnaies et Essais-Monnaies du Grand-Duche de Luxembourg 1796-1965,* Luxembourg, 1965.

Malaysia

IBNS, *Paper Money of the 20th Century*: Malaysia, Dallas, 1973.

C.C. LOW, *Malaya Banknote Catalog*, Racine, 1967.

WILLIAM SHAW AND ALI KASSIM HAJI, *Paper Currency of Malaysia*, etc, Kuala Lumpur, 1971.

SARON SINGH, KASSIM HAJI, C.C. LOW AND TONY LYE FONG, *Standard Catalogue of Coins and Banknotes of Malaysia*, etc, Kuala Lumpur, 1976.

STEPHEN TAN, *Standard Catalogue of Malaysia, Singapore, Brunei Coins and Paper Money*, 1998.

Maldive Islands

TIM J. BROWDER, *Maldive Islands Money*, Santa Monica, 1969.

Malta

EMMANUEL SAID, *Malta Coin, Banknote and Medal Catalogue*, Valletta, 1982.

Mexico

DOUGLAS AND DUANE, *The Complete Encyclopedia of Mexican Paper Money*, Iola, 1982.

CARLOS GAYTAN, *Billetes de Mexico*, Mexico City, 1965.

Paper Curency of Mexico, California, 1975.

Monaco

RAYMOND DE VOS, *History of the Monies, Medals and Tokens of Monaco*, New York, 1977.

Mongolia

E.D. GRIBANOV, *The Currency of the Mongolian People's Republic*, St. Louis, 1965.

Morocco

M. MUSZYNSKI AND H. SCHWEIKERT, *Le Papier-Monnaie du Maroc*, Paris, 1974.

Mozambique

BANCO NACIONAL ULTRAMARINO, *Papel-Moeda Para Mocambique*, 1877-1973, Lisbon, 1978.

COLIN R. OWEN, *The Banknotes of Mozambique*, Benoni, 1976.

Netherlands

J. MEVIUS AND F.G. LELIVELT, *De Nederlandse Bankbiljetten van 1814 tot Heden*, Amsterdam, 1981.

New Zealand

P.G. ECCLES, *The Premier Catalogue of New Zealand Coins and Banknotes*, Auckland, 1980.

ALISTAIR F. ROBB, *Coins, Tokens and Banknotes of New Zealand*, Wellington, 1976.

Nicaragua

BRIAN STICKNEY AND ALCEDO ALMANZAR, *The Coins and Paper Money of Nicaragua*, USA, 1974.

Papua New Guinea

DR WILLIAM J.D. MIRA, *From Cowrie to Kina,* Sydney, 1986.

Paraguay

DALE A. SEPPA, *Paraguayan Paper Money*, Chicago, 1974.

Peru

EDUARDO DARGENT, *El Billete en el Peru*, Lima, 1979.

Philippines

NEIL SHAFER, *A Guide Book of Philippines Paper Money*, Racine, 1964.

Poland

TADEUSZ JABLONSKI, *Polski Pieniadz Papierowny*, 1794-1948, Warsaw, 1964.

MARIAN KOWLSKI, *Katalog Banknotow Polskich 1916-1972*, Warsaw, 1973.

Portugal

FRANCISCO MALAFAYA, *Catalogo de Notafilia Portugal*, Porto, 1977.

Romania

V. COMAN, *Katalog der Rumanischen Banknoten*, Munster, 1967.

COL. R. IOAN DOGARU, *Catalogul Monedelor si Bancnotelar Romanesti*, Bucharest, 1978.

OCTAVIAN LUCHIAN, *Monede si Bancnote Romanesti*, Bucharest, 1977.

Russia

C. DENIS, *Catalogue des Monnaies Russes*, Paris, 1927.

N. KARDAKOFF, *Katalog der Geldscheine von Russland und der Baltischen Staaten*, Berlin, 1953.

N. NAVOLOCHKIN, *Soviet Numismatics*, Moscow, 1970.

Scotland

JAMES L. ANDERSON, *The Story of the Commercial Bank of Scotland*, Edinburgh, 1910.

C.W. BOASE, A Century of Banking in Dundee, Edinburgh, 1867.

JOHN BUCHANAN, *Glasgow Banking in Olden Times*, Glasgow, 1884.

S.G. CHECKLAND, *Scottish Banking: A History 1695-1973*, Glasgow, 1975.
DENNET *Scottish banknote catalogue*, Norwich, 2001
JAMES DOUGLAS, *Scottish Banknotes*, London, 1975.
20th Century Scottish Banknotes, Vols. 1 & 2, Carlisle, 1984.
SIR WILLIAM FORBES, *Memoirs of a Banking-House*, Edinburgh, 1859.
WILLIAM GRAHAM, *The One Pound Note in Scotland*, Edinburgh, 1911. *The Bank Note Circulation of Scotland*, Edinburgh, 1926.
TREVOR JONES, *20th Century Scottish Banknotes: Clydesdale Bank*, Carlisle, 1998.
ALEXANDER KEITH, *The North of Scotland Bank 1836-1936*, Aberdeen, 1936.
ANDREW W. KERR, *A History of Banking in Scotland*, London, 1884.
CHARLES A. MALCOLM, *The Bank of Scotland 1695-1945*, Edinburgh, 1945.
The History of the British Linen Bank, Edinburgh, 1950.
C. MUNN, *The Scottish Provincial Banking Companies, 1747-1864*, Edinburgh, 1981.
NEIL MUNRO, *The History of the Royal Bank of Scotland 1727-1927*, Edinburgh, 1928.
ROBERT | PRINGLE, *20th Century Scottish Banknotes: Royal Bank*, Carlisle, 1986.
ROBERT S. RAIT, *The History of the Union Bank of Scotland*, Glasgow, 1930.
J.M. REID, *The History of the Clydesdale Bank*, Glasgow, 1938.

South Africa

W. BERGMAN, *A History of the Regular and Emergency Paper Money Issues of South Africa*, Cape Town, 1971.
HAROLD P. LEVIUS, *Catalogue of South African Paper Money since 1900*, Johannesburg, 1972.

South East Asia

COLIN BRUCE, *Standard Guide to South Asian Coins and Paper Money Since 1556*, Iola, 1982.
HOWARD A. DANIEL, *The Catalogue and Guidebook of Southeast Asian Coins and Currency*, Ohio, 1978.

Spain

IBNS, *Paper Money of the 20th Century: Spanish Civil War*, St. Louis, 1978.
FLORIAN R. VELEZ-FRIAS AND JORGE A. VILA, *Catalogo del papel Moeda Espanol*, Madrid, 1975.
JOSE A. VICENTE, *Catalogo de Billetes Espanoles 1783-1977*, Madrid, 1977. *Catalogo Basico Monedas y Billetes 1869-1977*, Madrid, 1978.

Sri Lanka

H.W. CODRINGTON, *Ceylon Coins and Currency*, 1924, reprinted London 1999.

Surinam

THEO VAN ELMPT, *Surinam Paper Currency, 1760-1957*, London, 1998.

Sweden

SVEN FLODBERG, *Katalog over Sveriges Sedlar, 1858-1971*, Lund, 1972.
A. PLATBARZDIS, *Sveriges Sedlar 1661-1961*, Lund, 1963.
Sveriges Sedlar Enskilda Bankernas Sedlar 1831-1902, Lund, 1965.
LENNART WALLEN AND BJARNE AHLSTROM, *Sveriges Sedlar*, Stockholm, 1978.

Switzerland

URS GRAF, *Das Papiergeld der Schwiz, 1881-1068*, Munser, 1970 .

Thailand

BANK OF THAILAND, *Banknotes of Thailand*, Bangkok, 1972.
SILAS LITTLE, *Banknotes of Thailand*, Falls Church, USA, 1973.

Turkey

DR MINE EROL, *Osmanli Imparatorlugunda Kagit Para*, Ankara, 1970.
CUNEYT OLCER, *50 Yilin Turk Kagit Paralari*, Istanbul, 1973.

USA

FREDERICK BART, *Comprehensive Catalog of United States Paper Money Errors.*
ELVIRA AND VLADIMIR CLAIN-STEFANELLI, *American Banking*, Washington, 1975.
GROVER CRISWELL, *Confederate States of America Paper Money*, Florida, 1976.
W.P.DONLON, *United States Large Sizeer Pepr Money*, Utica, 1970.
RICHARD DOTY, *America's Money, America's Story*, Iola, 1998.
ROBERT FRIEDBERG, *Paper Money of the United States*, New York, various editions.
GENE HESSLER, *Comprehensive Catalog of US Paper Money US Essay, Proof and Specimen Notes*, 1979. *the Engraver's Line*
RON HORSTMAN, *Collecting National Bank Notes.*
CHESTER L. KRAUSE AND ROBERT F. LEMKE, *United States Paper Money*, Iola, 1999.
ERIC P. NEWMAN, *The Early Paper Money of America*, Iola, 1998.
ARLIE R. SLABAUGH *Confederate States Paper Money*, Iola, 2000

Uruguay

DALE A. SEPPA, *Uruguayan Paper Moneh*, Chicago, 1974.

Yemen

PETER SYMES, MURRAY HANEWICH AND KEITH STREET, *The Bank Notes of the Yemen*, Chester, 1998.

Yugoslavia

VOJISLAV MIHAILOVIC AND DRAGSOLAV GLOGONJAC, *Katalog Novca Srbije I Crne Gore 1868-1918*, Belgrade, 1973.
DIMITRI SPAJIC, *Paper Money of the Yugoslavian States*, USA, 1969.

Cheques and Postal Orders
STEPHEN CRIBB, *The Standard Catalogue of Postal Orders*, Ruislip, 1984.
JAMES DOUGLAS, *Collect British Cheques*, London, n.d. (c.1981)
A Collector's Guide to Cheques and Bills of Exchange, Carlisle, n.d.
HOWARD LUNN, *Promotional Postal Orders*, Nottingham,. N.d. [1990].
DAVID SHAW, *A Pictorial Guide to Cheque Collecting*, Nairn, 1985.
A Collector's Guide to British Cheques, Shrewsbury, 1986.

Museums and Libraries

Listed below are the Museums and Libraries in the UK which have coin collections and many also have banknotes or items of notaphilic interest on display or available to the general public. However, before setting off on a long journey it is advisable to contact the museum you wish to visit to check that any notes they have are available for viewing.

A

Anthropological Museum, University of Aberdeen, Broad Street, **Aberdeen,** AB9 1AS (01224 272014).

Curtis Museum (1855), High Street, **Alton,** Hants (01420 2802).

Ashburton Museum, 1 West Street, **Ashburton,** Devon.

Ashwell Village Museum (1930), Swan Street, **Ashwell,** Baldock, Herts.

Buckinghamshire County Museum (1862), Church Street, **Aylesbury,** Bucks (01296 88849).

B

Public Library and Museum (1948), Marlborough Road, **Banbury,** Oxon (01295 259855).

Museum of North Devon (1931), The Square, **Barnstaple,** EX32 8LN (01271 46747).

Roman Baths Museum, Pump Room, **Bath,** Avon (01225 461111 ext 2785).

Bagshaw Museum and Art Gallery (1911), Wilton Park, **Batley,** West Yorkshire (01924 472514).

Bedford Museum (1961), Castle Lane, **Bedford** (01234 353323).

Ulster Museum (1928), Botanic Gardens, **Belfast** BT9 5AB (01232 381251).

Berwick Borough Museum (1867), The Clock Block, Berwick Barracks, Ravensdowne, **Berwick**. TD15 1DQ (01289 330044).

Public Library, Art Gallery and Museum (1910), Champney Road, **Beverley,** Humberside (01482 882255).

City Museum and Art Gallery (1861), Chamberlain Square, **Birmingham** B3 3DH (0121 235 2834).

Blackburn Museum, Museum Street, **Blackburn,** Lancs (01254 667130).

Museum Collection, Town Hall, **Bognor Regis,** West Sussex.

Museum and Art Gallery,(1893), Civic Centre, **Bolton,** Lancashire (01204 22311 ext 2191).

Art Gallery and Museum, Central Library, Oriel Road, **Bootle,** Lancs.

Roman Town and Museum (1949) Main Street, **Boroughbridge,** N. Yorks. YO2 3PH (01423 322768).

The Museum (1929), The Guildhall, **Boston,** Lincs (01205 365954).

Natural Science Society Museum (1903), 39 Christchurch Road, **Bournemouth,** Dorset (01202 553525).

Bolling Hall Museum (1915), Bolling Hall Road, **Bradford,** West Yorkshire BD4 7LP (01274 723057).

Cartwright Hall Museum and Art Gallery (1904), Lister Park, **Bradford,** West Yorkshire BD9 4NS (01274 493313).

Museum and Art Gallery (1932), South Street, **Bridport,** Dorset (01308 22116).

The City Museum (1820), Queen's Road, **Bristol** BS8 1RL (0117 9 72256).

District Library and Museum (1891), Terrace Road, **Buxton,** Derbyshire SK17 6DU (01298 24658).

C

Fitzwilliam Museum (1816), Department of Coins and Medals, Trumpington Street, **Cambridge** (01223 332900).

National Museum & Galleries of Wales, Cathays Park, **Cardiff** (029 20397951).

Guildhall Museum (1979), Greenmarket, **Carlisle,** Cumbria (01228 819925).

Tullie House (1877), Castle Street, **Carlisle,** Cumbria (01228 34781).

Chelmsford and Essex Museum (1835), Oaklands Park, Moulsham Street, **Cheltenham,** Glos CM2 9AQ (01245 353066).

Town Gate Museum (1949), **Chepstow,** Gwent.

Grosvenor Museum (1886), Grosvenor Street, **Chester** (01244 21616).

Public Library (1879), Corporation Street, **Chesterfield,** Derbyshire (01246 2047).

Red House Museum (1919), Quay Road, **Christchurch,** Dorset (01202 482860).

Colchester and Essex Museum (1860), The Castle, **Colchester,** Essex (01206 712931/2).

D

Public Library, Museum and Art Gallery (1921), Crown Street, **Darlington,** Co Durham (01325 463795).

Borough Museum (1908), Central Park, **Dartford,** Kent (01322 343555).

Dartmouth Museum (1953), The Butterknowle, **Dartmouth,** Devon (01803 832923).

Museum and Art Gallery (1878), The Strand, **Derby** (01332 255586).

Museum and Art Gallery (1909), Chequer Road, **Doncaster,** South Yorkshire (01302 734293).

Dorset County Museum(1846), **Dorchester,** Dorset (01305 262735).

Central Museum (1884), Central Library, St James's Road, **Dudley,** West Midlands (01384 453576).

Burgh Museum (1835), The Observatory, Corberry Hill, **Dumfries** (01387 53374)**.**

Dundee Art Galleries and Museums (1873). Albert Square, **Dundee** DD1 1DA (01382 23141).

The Cathedral Treasury (995 AD), The College, **Durham** (0191-384 4854).

Durham Heritage Centre, St Mary le Bow, North Bailey, **Durham** (0191-384 2214).

E

Royal Museum of Scotland (1781), Queen Street, **Edinburgh** EH1 (0131 225 7534).

Royal Albert Memorial Museum (1868), Queen St, **Exeter** EX4 3RX (01392 265858).

G

Hunterian Museum (1807), Glasgow University, University Avenue, **Glasgow** G12 8QQ (041 339 8855).

Art Gallery and Museum (1888), Kelvingrove, **Glasgow** G3 (0141 357 3929).

Museum of Transport (1974), Kelvin Hall, Bunhouse Road, **Glasgow** G3 (0141 357 3929).

City Museum and Art Gallery (1859), Brunswick Road, **Gloucester** (01452 524131).

Guernsey Museum and Art Gallery, St Peter Port, **Guernsey** (01481 726518).

Guildford Museum (1898), Castle Arch, **Guildford,** Surrey GU1 3SX (01483 444750).

H

Gray Museum and Art Gallery, Clarence Road, **Hartlepool,** Cleveland (01429 268916).

Public Museum and Art Gallery (1890), John's Place, Cambridge Road, **Hastings,** East Sussex (01424 721952).

City Museum (1874), Broad Street, **Hereford** (01432 268121 ext 207).

Hertford Museum (1902), 18 Bull Plain, **Hertford** (01992 582686).

Honiton and Allhallows Public Museum (1946), High Street, **Honiton,** Devon (01404 44966).

Museum and Art Gallery (1891), 19 New Church Road, **Hove,** East Sussex (01273 779410).

Tolson Memorial Museum (1920), Ravensknowle Park, **Huddersfield,** West Yorkshire (01484 541455).

Hull and East Riding Museum (1928), 36 High Street, **Hull** (01482 593902). *Celtic, Roman and medieval coins and artifacts from local finds. Some later coins including tradesmen's tokens.*

I

The Manx Museum, Douglas, **Isle of Man** (01624 675522).

J

Jersey Museum, Weighbridge, St Helier, **Jersey** (01534 30511).

K

Dick Institute Museum and Art Gallery (1893), Elmbank Avenue, **Kilmarnock,** Ayrshire (01563 26401).

L

City Museum (1923), Old Town Hall, Market Square, **Lancaster** (01524 64637).

City Museum (1820), Municipal Buildings, The Headrow, **Leeds,** West Yorkshire (01532 478279).

Leicester Museum and Art Gallery (1849), New Walk, **Leicester** (01533 554100).

Pennington Hall Museum and Art Gallery, **Leigh,** Lancashire.

Museum and Art Gallery (1914), Broadway, **Letchworth,** Herts (01462 65647). *Ancient British coins minted at Camulodunum, Roman, me*

City Library, Art Gallery and Museum (1859), Bird Street, **Lichfield,** Staffs (01543 2177).

Liverpool Museum(1851), William Brown Street, **Liverpool** L3 8EN (0151 207 0001).

Bank of England Museum, Threadneedle Street, **London** EC2 (020-7601 5545).

British Museum(1752), HSBC Coin Gallery, Great Russell Street, **London** WC1 (020-7636 1555).

British Numismatic Society (1903), Warburg Institute, Woburn Square, **London** WC1.

Cuming Museum (1906), Walworth Road, **London** SE17 (020-7703 3324/5529).

Gunnersbury Park Museum (1927), Acton, **London** W3.

Horniman Museum and Library (1890), **London** Road, Forest Hill, London SE23 (020-7699 2339).

Imperial War Museum, Lambeth Road, **London** SE1 6HZ (020-7416 5000).

Sir John Soane's Museum (1833), 13 Lincoln's Inn Fields, **London** WC2 (020-7405 2107).

National Maritime Museum, Romney Road, Greenwich, **London** SE10 (020-8858 4422).

Victoria and Albert Museum (1852), South Kensington, **London** SW7 (020-7938 8441).

Ludlow Museum (1833). The Assembly Rooms. Castle Square, **Ludlow** (01584 873857).

Luton Museum and Art Gallery (1927), Wardown Park, **Luton**, Beds (01582 36941).

M

Museum and Art Gallery (1858), **Maidstone**, Kent (01622 754497).

The Manchester Museum (1868), The University, **Manchester** M13 (0161-275 2634).

Margate Museum (1923), The Old Town Hall, Market Place, **Margate**, Kent (01843 225511 ext 2520).

Montrose Museum and Art Gallery (1836). Panmure Place, **Montrose**, Angus DD10 8HE (01674 73232).

N

Newark-on-Trent Museum (1912), Appleton Gate, **Newark**, Notts (01636 702358).

Newbury District Museum, The Wharf, **Newbury**, Berkshire (01635 30511).

O

Heberden Coin Room, Ashmolean Museum (1683), **Oxford** (01865 278000).

P

Peterborough Museum (1881), Priestgate, **Peterborough**, Cambs (01733 340 3329).

City Museum and Art Gallery (1897), Drake Circus, **Plymouth**, Devon (01752 264878).

Waterfront Museum, 4 High Street, **Poole**, Dorset (01202 683138). *(view by appointment)*.

City Museum (1972), Museum Road, Old **Portsmouth** PO1 (023 80827261).

Harris Museum and Art Gallery (1893), Market Square, **Preston**, Lancashire (01772 58248).

R

Reading Museum and Art Gallery, (1883) Blagrave Street, **Reading**, Berks (01734 399809).

Rochdale Museum (1905), Sparrow Hill, **Rochdale**, Lancs (01706 41085).

Municipal Museum and Art Gallery (1893), Clifton Park, **Rotherham** (01709382121).

S

Saffron Walden Museum (1832) (1939), Museum Street, **Saffron** Walden, Essex (01799 522494).

Salisbury and South Wiltshire Museum (1861), The Cathedral Close, **Salisbury,** Wilts (01722 332151).

Scarborough Museum (1829), The Rotunda, Vernon Road, **Scarborough**, North Yorkshire (01723 374839).

Shaftesbury and Dorset Local History Museum (1946), 1 Gold Hill, **Shaftesbury**, Dorset (01747 52157).

City Museum (1875), Weston Park, **Sheffield** (0114 2 768588).

Rowley's House Museum, Barker Street, **Shrewsbury**, Salop (01743 361196).

Museum of Archaeology (1951), God's House Tower, Town Quay, **Southampton**, Hants (023 8022 0007).

Botanic Gardens Museum, Churchtown, **Southport,** Lancs (01704 87547).

Southwold Museum (1933), St Bartholomew's Green, **Southwold**, Suffolk (01502 722375).

Stamford Museum (1961), Broad Street, **Stamford**, Lincs (01780 66317).

Municipal Museum (1860), Vernon Park, Turncroft Lane, **Stockport**, Cheshire (0161 474 4460)

Stroud Museum (1899), Lansdown, **Stroud**, Glos (01453 376394).

Museum and Art Gallery (1846), Borough Road, **Sunderland,** Tyne & Wear (0191 514 1235).

Swansea Museum (1835), Victoria Road, **Swansea**, W. Glamorgan, SA1 1SN (0792 653765).

T

Tamworth Castle and Museum (1899), The Holloway, **Tamworth**, Staffs (01827 63563).

Somerset County Museum, Taunton Castle, **Taunton**, Somerset (01823 255510/320200). C

Thurrock Local History Museum (1956), Civic Square, **Tilbury**, Essex (01375 390000 ext 2414).

Royal Cornwall Museum (1818), River Street, **Truro,** Cornwall (01872 72205).

W

Wakefield Museum (1919), Wood Street, **Wakefield,** West Yorkshire (01924 295351).

Epping Forest District Museum, 39/41 Sun Street, **Waltham Abbey**, Essex EN 9.

Warrington Museum and Art Gallery (1848). Bold Street, **Warrington**, Cheshire, WA1 1JG (01925 30550).

Worcester City Museum (1833), Foregate Street, **Worcester** (01905 25371).

Wells Museum (18903), 8 Cathedral Green, **Wells,** Somerset (01749 3477).

Municipal Museum and Art Gallery (1878), Station Road, **Wigan**, Lancashire.

City Museum (1851), The Square, **Winchester**, Hants (01962 848269).

Wisbech and Fenland Museum (1835), Museum Square, **Wisbech,** Cambridgeshire (01945 583817).

Y

The Museum of South Somerset (1928), Hendford, **Yeovil,** Somerset (01935 24774).

Castle Museum (1938), **York** (01904 653611).

The Yorkshire Museum (1823), **York** (01904 629745).

Club directory

Most numismatic societies encompass banknotes in their agenda and many have regular speakers on the subject. Details given here are the names of the Numismatic Clubs or Societies, their dates of foundation, venue, days and times of meetings. Meetings are usually monthly unless otherwise stated. Finally, the telephone number of the club secretary is given; the names and addresses of club secretaries are withheld for security reasons, but full details may be obtained by writing to the Secretary of the British Association of Numismatic Societies, Philip Mernick, c/o Bush Boake Allen Ltd, Blackhorse Lane, London E17 5QP.

Banbury & District Numismatic Society (1967). Banbury British Rail Working Mens Club. 2nd Mon (exc Jul & Aug), 19.45. (01295 254451).

Bath & Bristol Numismatic Society (1950). Fry's Club, Keynsham, Bristol. 2nd Thu, 19.30. (0117 9039010).

Bedford Numismatic Society (1966). RAF Association Club, 93 Ashburnham Road, Bedford MK40 1EA. 3rd Mon, 19.30. (01234 228833/358369).

Bexley Coin Club (1968). St Martin's Church Hall, Erith Road, Barnehurst, Bexleyheath, Kent. 1st Mon (exc Jan & Aug), 20.00. (0208 303 0510).

Birmingham Numismatic Society (1964). Friend's Meeting House, Linden Lane, Bourneville,Birmingham. 1st Wed, 19.45. (0121 308 1616).

Matthew Boulton Society (1994). PO Box 395, Birmingham B31 2TB (0121 781 6558 fax 0121 781 6574).

Bradford & District Numismatic Society (1967). East Bowling Unity Club, Leicester Street, Bradford, West Yorkshire. 3rd Mon, 19.00. (01532 677151).

Brighton & Hove Coin Club (1971). Methodist Church Hall, St Patrick's Road, Hove, East Sussex. Last Wed (exc Dec), 20.00. (01273 419303).

British Cheque Collectors' Society (1980). John Purser, 71 Mile Lane, Cheylesmore, Coventry, West Midlands CV3 5GB.

British Numismatic Society (1903). Warburg Institute, Woburn Square, London WC1H 0AB. Monthly (exc Jul, Aug & Dec), 18.00. (01329 284661)

Cambridgeshire Numismatic Society (1946). Friends' Meeting House, 12 Jesus Lane (entrance in Park Street), Cambridge, CB5 8BA. 3rd Mon, Sept–June, 19.30. (01767 312112).

Chester & North Wales Coin & Banknote Society (1996). Liver Hotel, 110 Brook Street, Chester. 1st Tue, 20.00. (0151 478 4293)

Cheltenham Numismatic Society, The Reddings & District Community Association, North Road, The Reddings, Cheltenham. 3rd Mon, 19.45 (01242 673263)

Coin Correspondence Club (1988). Postal only. A.H. Chubb, 49 White Hart Lane, Barnes, London SW13 0PP. (0181-878 0472).

Crawley Coin Club (1969). Furnace Green Community Centre, Ashburnham Road, Furnace Green, Crawley, West Sussex. 1st Tue, 20.00. (01293 548671).

Crewe & District Coin & Medal Club (1968). Memorial Hall, Church Lane, Wistaston, Crewe, 2nd Tue (exc Jan & July), 19.30. (01270 69836).

Darlington & District Numismatic Society (1968). Darlington Arts Centre, Vane Terrace, Darlington, Co Durhm. 3rd Wed, 19.30. (01609 772976).

Derbyshire Numismatic Society (1964). The Friends' Meeting House, St Helens Street, Derby. 3rd Mon (exc August), 19.45. (01283 211623).

Devon & Exeter Numismatic Society (1965). Red Cross Centre, Butts Road, Heavitree, Exeter, Devon. 3rd Tue, 19.30. (01392 461013).

Edinburgh Numismatic Society (1996). Department of History and Applied Arts, Royal Museum of Scotland, Chambers Street, Edinburgh EH1 1JF. 3rd Mon, 19.30. (0131 225 7534).

Enfield & District Numismatic Society (1969). Millfield House Arts Centre, Silver Street, Edmonton, London N18 1PJ. 3rd Mon, 20.00. (0181-340 0767).

Essex Numismatic Society (1966). Chelmsford & Essex Museum, Moulsham Street, Chelmsford, Essex. 4th Fri (exc Dec), 20.00. (01277 656627).

Glasgow & West of Scotland Numismatic Society (1947). The College Club, University of Glasgow, University Avenue, Glasgow G12. 2nd Thu, Oct–May, 19.30. (0141 633 2564).

Harrow & North West Middlesex Numismatic Society (1968). Harrow Arts Centre, Hatch End Harrow, Middlesex. 2nd and 4th Mon, 20.00. (020 8952 8765).

Havering Numismatic Society (1967). Fairkytes Arts Centre, Billet Lane, Hornchurch, Essex. 1st Tue, 19.30. (01708 704201).

Hayes & District Coin Club. The United Reformed Church Hall, Swakeleys Road, Ickenham, Middlesex. 3rd Thu, 19.45. (0181-422 9178).

Horncastle & District Coin Club (1963). Bull Hotel, Bull Ring, Horncastle, Lincs. 2nd Thu (exc Aug), 19.30. (01754 2706).

Huddersfield Numismatic Society (1947). Huddersfield Library, Princess Alexandra Walk, Huddersfield, West Yorkshire. 1st Mon (exc Jul & Aug), 19.30. (01484 226300).

Hull & District Numismatic Society (1967). The Young People's Institute, George Street, Hull. Monthly (exc Aug & Dec), 19.30. (01482 441933).

International Bank Note Society (1961). Victory Services Club, 63–79 Seymour Street, London W1. Last Thu (exc Dec), 18.00. (020-8360 2759).

International Bank Note Society, Scottish Chapter (1995). West End Hotel, Palmerston Place, Edinburgh. Last Sat (exc Dec), 14.30 (0141 642 0132).

Ipswich Numismatic Society (1966). Ipswich Citizens Advice Bureau, 19 Tower Street, Ipswich, Suffolk. 3rd Wed, 19.30. (01473 711158).

Kent Towns Numismatic Society (1913). Adult Education Centre, 9 Sittingbourne Road (Maidstone) and King's School Preparatory School, King Edward Road (Rochester). 1st Fri of month, 19.30 alternately at Maidstone and Rochester. (01622 843881).

Kingston Numismatic Society (1966). King Athelstan's School, Villiers Road, Kingston-upon-Thames, Surrey. 3rd Thu (exc Jan), 19.30. (020-8397 6944).

Lancashire & Cheshire Numismatic Society (1933). Manchester Central Library, St Peter's Square, Manchester M2 5PD. Monthly, Sep-June, Wed (18.30) or Sat (14.30). (0161 445 2042).

Lincolnshire Numismatic Society (1932). Grimsby Bridge Club, Bargate, Grimsby, South Humberside. 4th Wed (exc Aug), 19.30.

London Numismatic Club (1947). Institute of Archaeology, 31–34 Gordon Square, London WC1H 0PY. Monthly, 18.30.

Loughborough Coin & Search Society (1964). Wallace Humphry Room, Shelthorpe Community Centre, Loughborough, Leics. 1st Thu, 19.30. (01509 261352).

Merseyside Numismatic Society (1947). The Lecture Theatre, Liverpool Museum, William Brown Street, Liverpool L3 8EN. Monthly (exc July & Aug), 19.00. (0151-929 2143).

Mid Lanark Coin Circle (1969). Hospitality Room, The Civic Centre, Motherwell, Lanarkshire. 4th Thu, Sep–Apr (exc Dec), 19.30. (0141-552 2083).

Monmouthshire Numismatic Society. W. R. Lysaght Institute, Corporation Road, Newport. 2nd Wed, 19.30. (029 20 561564)

Morecambe & Lancaster Numismatic Society. Monthly, 19.30. (01524 411036).

Newbury Coin & Medal Club (1971). Monthly, 20.00. (01635 41233).

Northampton Numismatic Society (1969). Old Scouts RFC, Rushmere Road, Northampton. 3rd Mon, 20.00.

Norwich Numismatic Society (1967). Assembly House, Theatre Street, Norwich, Norfolk. 3rd Mon, 19.30. (01493 651577).

Nottinghamshire Numismatic Society (1948). The Meeting Room, County Library, Angel Row, Nottingham NG1 6HP. 2nd Tue (Sep-Apr), 19.30. (0115 9257674).

Nuneaton & District Coin Club (1968). United Reformed Church Room, Coton Road, , Nuneaton, Warwickshire. 2nd Tue, 19.30. (01203 371556).

Orders & Medals Research Society (1942). National Army Museum, Royal Hospital Road, Chelsea, London SW3. Monthly, 14.30. (020-8680 2701).

Ormskirk & West Lancashire Numismatic Society (1970). Eagle & Child, Ormskirk. Lancs. 1st Thu, 20.15. (01704 531266).

Peterborough Coin & Medal Club (1967). The Club Room, APV-Baker Social Club, Alma Road, Peterborough, Cambs. Last Tue (exc July & Aug), 19.30.

Plymouth Coin & Medal Club (1970). RAFA Club, 5 Ermington Terrace, Mutley Plain, Plymouth, Devon. 4th Wed (exc Dec), 19.30. (01752 362859).

Postal Order Society, Mal Tedds, 1 Fairham Court, Wilford, Nottingham, NG11 7EN (0115 981 5639).

Preston & District Numismatic Society (1965). Eldon Hotel, Eldon Street, Preston, Lancs. 1st and 3rd Tue, 20.00. (012572 66869).

Reading Coin Club (1964). Reading Library, Abbey Square, Reading. 1st Tue, 20.00. (0118 9332843).

Redbridge Numismatic Society (1968). Gants Hill Library, Cranbrook Road, Ilford, Essex. 4th Wed, 19.30. (020-8554 5486).

Rochford Hundred Numismatic Society. Civic Suite, Rayleigh Town Hall, Rayleigh, Essex. 2nd Thu, 20.00. (01702 230950).

Romsey Numismatic Society (1969). Romsey WM Conservative Club, Market Place, Romsey, Hants SO5 8NA. 4th Fri (exc Dec), 19.30. (01703 253921).

Rotherham & District Coin Club (1982). Rotherham Art Centre, Rotherham, South Yorkshire. 1st Wed, 19.00. (01709 528179).

Royal Mint Coin Club, PO Box 500, Cardiff CF1 1HA (01443 222111).

Royal Numismatic Society (1836). Society of Antiquaries, Piccadilly, London W1. Monthly (Oct-June), 17.30. Joe Cribb, Coins and Medals, British Museum, London WC1B 3DG (020-7323 8585).

Rye Coin Club (1955). Rye Further Education Centre, Lion Street, Rye, East Sussex. 2nd Thu (Oct-Dec, Feb-May), 19.30. (01424 422974).

St Albans & Hertfordshire Numismatic Society (1948). St Michael's Parish Centre, Museum Entrance, Verulamium Park, St Albans, Herts AL3 4SL. 2nd Tue (exc Aug), 19.30. (01727 862060).

Sheffield Numismatic Society. Telephone for venue. 2nd Wed, 19.00. (0114 2817129)

South East Hants Numismatic Society. Havant Conservative Club, East Street, Havant. 1st Fri. (01329 389419).

South Manchester Numismatic Society (1967). Nursery Inn, Green Lane, Heaton Mersey, Stockport. Fortnightly Mon, 20.00. (0161-485 7017).

S. Wales & Monmouthshire Numismatic Society (1958). The W. R. Lysaght Institute, Corporation Road, Newport. 2nd Wed, 19.30. (029 20561564).

Torbay & District Coin Club (1967). British Rail Social Club, Brunel Road, Newton Abbott, Devon TQ12 4PB. 1st Tue, 1945. (01803 326497).

Tyneside Numismatic Society (1954). RAFA Club, Eric Nelson House, 16 Berwick Road, Gateshead, Tyne & Wear. 2nd Wed, 19.30. (0191 3719700).

Wessex NS (1948). Hotel Bristowe, Grange Road, Southbourne, Bournemouth, Dorset. 2nd Thurs (exc Aug), 19.45. (020 7731 1702).

Wiltshire Numismatic Society (1965). Raven Inn, Poulshot, Nr Devizes, Wiltshire. 3rd Mon, Mar-Dec, 20.00. (01225 703143).

Worthing & District Numismatic Society (1967). Kingsway Hotel, Marine Parade, Worthing, West Sussex BN11 3QQ. 3rd Thu, 19.30. (01634 260114).

Yorkshire Numismatic Society (1909). Swarthmore College, Woodhouse Square, Leeds. 1st Sat (exc Jan, Aug & Dec) (01943 463049).

Many Society meetings are featured in the "What's On" Calendar in COIN NEWS every month.

directory of Auctioneers

Listed here are the major UK auction houses which handle coins, medals, banknotes and other items of numismatic interest. Many of them hold regular public auctions, whilst others handle numismatic material infrequently. A number of companies also hold regular Postal Auctions—these are marked with a P.

Baldwin's Auctions Ltd

11 Adelphi Terrace, London WC2N 6BJ (020-7930 6879 fax 020-7930 9450). Website: www.baldwin.sh.

Banking Memorabilia

PO Box 14, Carlisle CA3 8DZ (0169 7476465).

A. F. Brock & Company

269 London Road, Hazel Grove, Stockport, Cheshire SK7 4PL (0161-456 5050/5112). Website: www.afbrock.co.uk

Christie, Manson & Wood Ltd

8 King Street, St James's, London SW1Y 6QT (020-7 839 9060).

Corbitts

5 Moseley Sreet, Newcastle upon Tyne NE1 1YE (0191-232 7268 fax 0191-261 4130).

Croydon Coin Auctions

272 Melfort Road, Thornton Heath, Surrey CR7 7RR (020-8656 4583/020-8684 6515 fax 020-8656 4583). Website: www.croydoncoinauctions.co.uk.

Dix Noonan Webb

1 Old Bond Street, London W1XZ 3TD (020 7499 5022 fax 020 7499 5023) Website: www.dnw.co.uk.

Edinburgh Coin Shop

11 West Crosscauseway, Edinburgh EH8 9JW (0131 668 2928 fax 0131 668 2926).

Fellows & Sons

Augusta House, 19 Augusta Street, Hockley, Birmingham B18 6JA (0121-212 2131).

B. Frank & Son

3 South Avenue, Ryton, Tyne & Wear NE40 3LD (0191 413 8749 fax 0191 413 2957). e-mail: bfrankandson@aol.com

Gillio Coins International

1013 State Street, Santa Barbara, CA 93101, USA, London contact Eric Green 020-7586 3964).

Glendining & Co

101 New Bond Street, London W1Y 9LG (020 7 493 2445 fax 020 7491 9181).

Graves, Son & Pilcher Fine Arts

71 Church Road, Hove, East Sussex BN3 2GL (01273 735266 fax 01273 723813).

Hoods Postal Coin Auctions

23 High Street, Kilbirnie, Ayrshire KA25 7EX (fax/tel 01505 682157). **P**

Kleeford Coin Auctions

19 Craythorns Crescent, Dishforth, Thirsk YO7 3LY. (tel/fax 01845 577977).

W. H. Lane & Son

65 Morrab Road, Penzance, Cornwall TR18 2QT (01736 61447 fax 0736 50097) also: Trafalgar House, Malpas Road, Truro, Cornwall TR1 1QH (0872 223379).

Lawrence Fine Art Auctioneers

South Street, Crewkerne, Somerset TA18 8AB (01460 73041).

David Lay

The Penzance Auction House, Alverton, Penzance, Cornwall TR18 4RE (01736 61414 fax 01736 60035).

Lockdale Coins

36 Upper Orwell Street, Ipswich IP4 1BR. (01473 218588). Website: www.lockdales.co.uk.

London Coin Auctions

31 Reigate Way, Wallington, Surrey SM6 8NU (020 8 688 5297). Website: www.londoncoins.co.uk.

Neales

192–194 Mansfield Road, Nottingham NG1 3HU (0115 9624141 fax 0115 9856890).

Phillips

101 New Bond Street, London W1Y 9LG (020-7629 1877 fax 020-7409 3466). Website: phillips-auctions.com

R & W Coin Auctions

307 Bretch Hill, Banbury, Oxon OX16 0JD (01295 275128).

Sheffield Coin Auctions

7 Beacon Close, Sheffield S9 1AA (0114 2 490442).

Henry Spencer & Sons

20 The Square, Retford, Notts DN22 6BX (01777 708633 fax 01777 709299).

Spink & Son Ltd

69 Southampton Row, Bloomsbury, London WC1B 4ET (020 7563 4000 fax 20 7563 4066). Website: www.spink-online.com

Sussex Auction Galleries

59 Perrymount Road, Haywards Heath, West Sussex RH16 3DS (01444 414935 fax 01444

Warwick & Warwick

Chalon House, Scarbank, Millers Road, Warwick CV34 5DB (01926 499031 fax 01926 491906) E-mail: info@warwickandwarwick.com

Whytes

38 Molesworth Street, Dublin 2, Republic of Ireland (3531 676 2888 fax 676 2880). Website: www.whytes.ie.

directory of
Dealers

The dealers listed below have comprehensive stocks of papermoney, unless otherwise stated. Specialities, where known, are noted. Many of those listed are postal dealers only, so to avoid disappointment always make contact by telephone or mail in the first instance, particularly before travelling any distance.

Abbreviations:

ADA—Antiquities Dealers Association

ANA—American Numismatic Association

BADA—British Antique Dealers Association

BNTA—British Numismatic Trade Association

IAPN—International Association of Professional Numismatists

IBNS—International Bank Note Society

P—Postal only

L—Publishes regular lists

F—Fairs

A. Ackroyd (IBNS)

62 Albert Road, Parkstone, Poole, Dorset BH12 2DB (tel/fax 01202 739039). *P. L. Banknotes, cheques etc.*

David Allen Coins and Collectables

PO Box 125, Pinner, Middlesex HA5 2TX (020 866 6796). *P. L. British and world coins, tokens, banknotes.*

Keith Austin (IBNS)

PO Box 89, Carlise, Cumbria CA3 0GH (01228 819149). L. *Banknotes.* E-mail: kaustin@kabc.freeserve.co.uk

Banking Memorabilia (IBNS)

PO Box 14, Carlisle, Cumbria (0169 747 6465). 09.00–18.00 (not Sun). *Cheques, banknotes, related ephemera. auctions.*

D. G. Barney

Greenfield, Colyton Hill, Colyton, Devon EX24 6HY (01297 552 702). *British and world coins, tokens and banknotes.* E-mail: doug.barney@ondigital.com

Bath Stamp and Coin Shop (BNTA)

Pulteney Bridge, Bath, Avon BA2 4AY (01225 463073). Mon-Sat 09.30–17.30. *British, world coins and banknotes.*

R. P. & P. J. Beckett

Maesyderw, Capel Dewi, Llandyssul, Dyfed SA44 4PJ. *P. World crowns, coin sets and banknotes.*

Berkshire Coin Centre

35 Castle Street, Reading, Berkshire RG1 7SB (01734 575593). 10.00–16.00 weekdays, half-day Sat. *British and world coins and banknotes.*

Barry Boswell (IBNS)

24 Townsend Lane, Upper Boddington, Daventry, Northants NN11 6DR (01327 61877). *P. L. British and world banknotes.* E-mail: Barry.Boswell@btinternet.com.

A. F. Brock & Company

269 London Road, Hazel Grove, Stockport, Cheshire SK7 4PL (0161 456 5050/5112. Mon-Sat 09.30–17.30. Website: www.afbrock.co.uk

E. J. & C. A. Brooks (BNTA, IBNS)

44 Kiln Road, Thundersley, Essex SS7 1TB (01268 753835). Any time up to 23.00. *L. British coins and banknotes.*

Iain Burn (IBNS)

2 Compton Gardens, 53 Park Road, Camberley, Surrey GU15 2SP (01276 23304). *England and treasury notes.*

Cambridge Stamp Centre Ltd

9 Sussex Street, Cambridge CB4 4HU (01223 63980). Mon-Sat 09.00–17.30. *British coins and banknotes.*

Castle Galleries

81 Castle Street, Salisbury, Wiltshire SP1 3SP (01722 333734). Tue, Thu Fri 09.00–17.00, Sat 09.30–16.00. *British coins, banknotes, medals and tokens.*

M. Coeshaw

PO Box 115, Leicester LE3 8JJ (01533 873808). *P.*

Coin & Collectors Centre

PO Box 22, Pontefract, West Yorkshire WR8 1YT (01977 704112). *P. British coins and banknotes.*

Coincraft (ANA, IBNS)

44/45 Great Russell Street, London WC1B 3LU (020 7636 1188 and 020 7637 8785 fax 020 7323 2860). Mon-Fri 09.30–17.00, Sat 10.00–14.30. L (*newspaper format*). *Coins and banknotes.* Website: www.coincraft.com.

Coinote Services Ltd

PO Box 53, Sorting Office, Clarke Street, Hartlepool TS26 NYL (01429 273044). *P. L. Coins and banknotes 1615 todate. Accessories and books.*

Coins of Beeston

PO Box 19, Beeston, Notts BG9 2NE. *P. L. Tokens, medals and paranumismatics.*

The Collector

242 High Street, Orpington, Kent BR6 0LZ (01689 890045). Mon-Sat 09.30–17.00 (closed Tue). *Coins, medals, banknotes, badges, militaria, cigarette cards etc*

Collectors' Forum

237 South Street, Romford, Essex RM1 2BE (01708 723357). Mon-Sat 09.30-18.00 Thu 09.30-14.00. *British coins, medals and banknotes.*

Collectors Gallery (BNTA, IBNS)

Castle Hall, Castle Gates, Shrewsbury SY1 2AD (01743 272140 fax 01743 366041). Mon-Fri 09.00–18.00, half-day Sat. *Coins and banknotes. Accessories and related books. Stockist of Abafil Coin Cases.* www.collectors-gallery.co.uk.

Corbitts (BNTA)

5 Mosley Street, Newcastle Upon Tyne NE1 1YE (0191 232 7268 fax: 0191 261 4130). *Dealers and auctioneers of all coins, medals and banknotes.*

G. D. Courtenay

58 New Peachey Lane, Uxbridge, Middlesex UB8 3SX. *P. L. Coins, medals, tokens and banknotes.*

Davidson Monk Fairs

PO Box 201, Croydon, Surrey CR9 7AQ (020 8656 4583). *Organiser of monthly fairs at the Commonwealth Institute, Kensington High Street, London W8.*

Paul Davies Ltd (ANA, BNTA, IAPN)

PO Box 17, Ilkley, West Yorkshire LS29 8TZ (01943 603116). *P. World coins and banknotes.*

Dei Gratia

PO Box 3568, Buckingham MK18 4ZS (01280 848000). *P. L. Pre-Roman to modern coins, antiquities, banknotes.*

Clive Dennett (BNTA, IBNS)

66 St Benedicts Street, Norwich, Norfolk NR2 4AR (01603 624315). Mon-Fri 09.00–17.30, Sat 09.00–16.00 (closed Thu). *L. World paper money.*

C. J. Denton (ANA, BNTA, FRNS)

PO Box 25, Orpington, Kent BR6 8PU (01689 873690). *P. World coins.*

Dolphin Coins (ANA)

22 High Street, Leighton Buzzard, Bedfordshire, LU7 7EB. (01525 383822 Fax: 01525 383872). Mon-Fri 09.30– 17.00. Sat appt only. *L. British and world coins and banknotes.* Website: www.dolphincoins.com.

Dorset Coin Co Ltd (BNTA)

193 Ashley Road, Parkstone, Poole, Dorset BH14 9DL (01202 739064, fax 01202 739230). *P. L. Separate coin and banknote lists.*

Edinburgh Coin Shop (ANA)

11 West Crosscauseway, Edinburgh EH8 9JW (0131 668 2928 fax 0131 668 2926). Mon-Sat 10.00–17.30. *L. World coins, medals and banknotes. Postal auctions.*

ELM

15 Phillimore Walk, Kensington, London W8 7SA (020 7937 8484)P. *Egyptian Banknotes.*

Ely Stamp & Coin Shop

27 Fore Hill, Ely, Cambs CB7 1AA (01353 663919). Mon, Wed-Sat 09.30–17.30. *World coins, medals and banknotes.*

Evesham Stamp & Coin Centre

Magpie Antiques, Paris House, 61 High Street, Evesham, Worcs WR11 4DA (01386 41631). Mon-Sat 09.00–17.30. *British coins and banknotes.*

Richard N. Flashman

54 Ebbsfleet Walk, Gravesend, Kent, DA11 9EW. *L. P. British banknotes.*

Format of Birmingham Ltd (ANA, BNTA, IAPN, IBNS)

18-19 Bennetts Hill, Birmingham B2 5QJ (0121 643 2058). Mon-Fri 09.30-7.00. *L. Coins, tokens and medals.*

Fox & Co (BNTA)

30 Princes Street, Yeovil, Somerset BA20 1EQ (01935 72323). Mon-Sat 09.00-17.30. *British, world coins, banknotes and numismatic books.*

B. Frank & Son (ANA, IBNS)

3 South Avenue, Ryton, Tyne & Wear NE40 3LD (0191 413 8749). *P. L. Banknotes and cheques, coins of the world. Organiser of the North of England Coin & Banknote fair.* E-mail: bfrankandson@aol.com

John Gaunt

21 Harvey Road, Bedford MK41 9LF (01234 217685). By appointment. *Numismatic books.*

Alistair Gibb (IBNS)

5 West Albert Road, Kirkcaldy, Fife KY1 1DL (01592 269045). *P. L. Banknotes and books on banking.*

Glance Back Books

17 Upper Street, Chepstow, Gwent NP6 5EX (01291 626562). 10.30–17.30. *World coins, medals, banknotes.*

Glendining's (ANA, BNTA)

101 New Bond Street, London W1Y 9LG (020 7493 2445). Mon-Fri 08.30-17.00, Sat 08.30–13.00. *Auctioneers.* Website: phillips-auctions.com

K. Goulborn

12 Sussex ST. Ryl, Clwyd (01745 338112 or 01745 344856). *P. L. British coins and banknotes.*

Ian Gradon

0191 3719 700. www.worldnotes.co.uk. *P. L. World bank notes.*

Granta Stamp & Coin Shop

28 Magdalene Street, Cambridge CB3 0AF (01223 315044) Mon-Sat 10.30-18.30. *English coins and banknotes.*

Grantham Coins (BNTA)

PO Box 60, Grantham, Lincs (01476 870565). *P. L. English coins and banknotes.*

Eric Green—Agent in UK for Ronald J. Gillio Inc,

1013 State Street, Santa Barbara, California, USA (020 8907 0015, Mobile 0468 454948). *Gold coins, banknotes*

Ian Haines

PO Box 45, Hereford, HR2 7YP (01432 268178). *P. L. British and foreign coins and banknotes.*

A. D. Hamilton & Co (ANA, BNTA)

7 St Vincent Place, Glasgow G1 5JA (0141 221 5423, fax 0141 248 6019). Mon-Sat 09.00-17.30. *British and World coins and banknotes.* Website: www.adhamiltons.com

John Harvey (IBNS)

PO Box 118, Bury St. Edmunds, IP33 2NE (01284 761894). *British Isles, Scotland, Channel Islands.*

Craig Holmes

6 Marlborough Drive, Bangor, Co Down BT19 1HB. *P. L. Low cost banknotes of the world.*

R. G. Holmes

11 Cross Park, Ilfracombe, Devon EX34 8BJ (01271 864474). *P. L. Coins, modern world crowns and foreign banknotes.*

Homeland Holding Ltd (IBNS)

Homeland, St John, Jersey, Channel Islands JE3 4AB (01534 65339). Mon-Fri 09.00-2.00. *World coins.*

HTSM Coins

26 Dosk Avenue, Glasgow G13 4LQ. *P. L. British and foreign coins and banknotes.*

Intercol London (ANA, BNTA, IBNS)

43 Templars Crescent, London N3 3QR (020 7349 2207). *P. Paper money of the world.*

Peter Ireland Ltd (BNTA, IBNS)

31 Clifton Street, Blackpool, Lancs FY1 1JQ (01253 21588 fax 0253 300232). Mon-Sat 09.00-17.30.*British and world coins, medals and tokens (some banknotes).*

JAK (IBNS)

31 Vapron Road, Mannamead, Plymouth, Devon PL3 5NJ (01752 665405). *P. L. GB and Commonwealth banknotes.*

Richard W. Jeffery

Trebehor, Porthcurno, Penzance, Cornwall TR19 6LS (01736 871263). *P. British and world coins and banknotes.*

KB Coins (BNTA)

50 Lingfield Road, Martins Wood, Stevenage, Herts SG1 5SL (01438 312661). 09.00–18.00 by appointment only. *L. Mainly British coins and banknotes.*

Peter Licence

31 Reigate Way, Wallington, Surrey SM6 8NU (020 8688 5297). *P. British and World coins.*

Lighthouse Publications (UK)

4 Beaufort Road, Reigate, Surrey RH2 9DJ (01737 244222 Fax 0737 24743). *L. Manufacturers and stockists of albums, cabinets and accessories.*

Lindner Publications Ltd

13 Fore Street, Hayle, Cornwall TR27 4DX (01736 751914 fax: 01736 751911). Mon–Fri 09.00–13.00. *L. Manufacturers of albums, cabinets and accessories.* Website: www.stampaccessories.net.

Lockdale Coins

36 Upper Orwell Street, Ipswich. (01473 218588). *L.* (Shop open 9.30–4.30 Mon–Sat). *World coins, medals, banknotes and accessories.* Website: www.lockdales.co.uk.

Stephen Lockett

59 Cedar Drive, Sutton at Hone, Kent DA4 9EW (01322 861 228). *British and world coins.*

Clive Maxwell-Yates

21 Nicolas Road, Chorlton Manchester, M21 1LG (0161 881 7015). *P. L. World banknotes.*

Michael Coins

6 Hillgate Street, London W8 7SR (020 7727 1518). Mon-Fri 10.00-17.00. *World coins and banknotes.*

Graeme & Linda Monk (ANA, BNTA)

PO Box 201, Croydon, Surrey, CR9 7AQ (020 8656 4583 fax 020 8656 4583). *P. Fair organisers.*

Peter Morris

1 Station Concourse, Bromley North Station, Bromley, BR1 1NN or PO Box 223, Bromley, BR1 4EQ (0020 8313 3410 Fax: 020 8466 8502). Mon-Fri 10.00–18.00, Sat 0900-14.00 or by appointment. *L. British and world coins and banknotes, numismatic books.* Website: www.petermorris.co.uk.

Colin Narbeth & Son Ltd (ANA, IBNS)

20 Cecil Court, Leicester Square, London WC2N 4HE (020 7379 6975). Mon-Sat 10.30-17.00. *World banknotes.* Website: www.colin-narbeth.com.

New Forest Leaves

Bisterne Close, Burley, Ringwood, Hants BH24 4BA (014253 3315). *Publishers of numismatic books.*

Notability (IBNS)

'Mallards', Chirton, Devizes, Wilts SN10 3QX (01380 723961). *P. L. Banknotes of the world.* Website: www.notability.org.uk.

Michael O'Grady (IBNS)

PO Box 307, Pinner, Middlesex HA5 4XT (020 8428 4002). *P. British and world paper money.* E-mail: mike@ogrady.clara.co.uk

Penrith Coin & Stamp Centre

37 King Street, Penrith, Cumbria CA11 7AY (01768 64185). Mon-Sat 09.00–17.30. *World coins and notes.*

Pentland Coins (IBNS)

Pentland House, 92 High Street, Wick, Caithness KW14 L5. *P. British, world coins and world banknotes.*

John Pettit Pty Ltd

GPO Box 4593, Sydney 2001, Australia. (00612 9235 0888) www.johnpettit.com. *P. L. Rare banknote specialist*

Phil Phipps (IBNS)

PO Box 31, Emsworth, Hants PO10 7WE (tel/fax 01243 376086). *P. L. World and German banknotes.* E-mail: phillip@worldcurrency.cc.

David Pratchett

Trafalgar Square Collectors Centre, 7 Whitcombe Street, London WC2H 7HA. (020 7930 1979). Mon-Fri 10.00–7.30. *Specialist in world coins and banknotes.* Website: www.coinsonline.co.uk.

George Rankin Coin Co Ltd (ANA, BNTA)

325 Bethnal Green Road, London E2 6AH (020 7729 1280 fax 020 7729 5023). Mon-Sat 10.00-18.00 (half-day Thu). *World coins and banknotes.*

Mark T. Ray (formerly MTR Coins)

22a Kingsnorth Close, Newark, Notts NG24 1PS. (01636 703152). *P. British coins and banknotes.*

Bill Rosedale

17 Priory JClose, Abbots Park, Chester CH1 4BX (01244 382554) *P. L. World paper money.* E-mail: bill@banknotes40freeserve.com.

Royal Mint

Llantrisant , Pontyclun, Mid Galmorgan, CF7 8YT. 01443 222111. www.royalmint.com. *P. L. Agent for Debden Security Printing (new banknote issues). Quarterly colour magazine for members.*

Safe Albums (UK) Ltd

Freepost (RG 1792), Wokingham, Berks RG11 1BR (01734 328976 fax 01734 328612). *P. Banknote albums, coin holders, etc.*

Simmons Gallery (ANA, BNTA, IBNS)

53 Lamb's Conduit Street, London WC1N 3NB (020 7831 2080 fax 020 7831 2090). *Organisers of the London Coin Fair, Cumberland Hotel, Marble Arch, London W1. L. Coins, tokens and medals.* Website: simmonsgallery.co.uk.

E. Smith (ANA, IBNS)

PO Box 348, Lincoln LN6 0TX (01522 684681 fax 01522 689528). *P. Organisewr of the Morley, Leeds, monthly coin fair. World coins and paper money.*

Spink & Son Ltd (ANA, BNTA, IAPN, IBNS)

Southampton Row, Bloomsbury, London WC1B 4ET (020 7563 4000 Fax: 020 7563 4066. Mon-Sat 09.30–17.30. *Ancient, medieval and modern world coins, orders, medals and decorations, banknotes and numismatic books—new and secondhand.*

Website: www.spink-online.com.

Stamp & Collectors Centre

404 York Town Road, College Town, Camberley, Surrey GU15 4PR (01276 32587 fax 01276 32505). Mon, Tue, Thu, Sat 09.00–17.00, Wed, Fri 09.00–1900. *World coins, medals and banknotes.*

Sterling Coins & Medals

2 Somerset Road, Boscombe, Bournemouth, Dorset BH7 6JH (01202 423881). Mon-Sat 09.30–16.30 (closed Wed). *World coins and banknotes.*

Strawbridge

Tanglewood, Ivy Tree Hill, Stokeinteignhead, Newton Abbott, Devon TQ12 4QH (01626 873783). *P. L. Coins, tokens, medals, banknotes.*

Trafalgar Square Collectors' Centre (ANA, BNTA, LM, OMRS)

7 Whitcomb Street, Trafalgar Square, London WC2H 7HA (020 7930 1979). Mon-Fri 10.00–17.30. *World coins and commemorative medals. A limited stock of world banknotes.*

Vera Trinder Ltd

38 Bedford Street, Strand, London WC2E 9EU (020 7836 2365/6). Mon-Fri 08.30-17.30. *L. Catalogues and books, albums, envelopes, cases and accessories.*

Vista World Banknotes

5 Greenfields Way, Burley-in-Wharfdale, Ilkley, W.Yorks, LS29 7RB. *World Notes list.* E-mail: vistabanknotes@barclays.net.

Pam West (IBNS, ANA, PCDA)

PO Box 257, Sutton, Surrey SM3 9WW (020 8641 3224). *P. L. English banknotes, British banknotes accessories.* Website: west-banknotes.co.uk.

West Cornwall Stamp Centre

13 Fore Street, Hayle, Cornwall TR27 4DX (01736 751910 fax: 01736 751911. *L. Coin Accessories.*

West Essex Coin Investments (BNTA, IBNS)

Croft Cottage, Station Road, Alderholt, Fordingbridge, Hants SP6 3AZ (01425 656 459). *P. L. British and World coins and paper money.*

R & J White (IBNS)

29 Shortacre, Basildon, Essex SS14 2LR (01268 522923). *P. L. Banknotes and world ephemera.*

Trevor Wilkin

Po Box 182, Cammeray, NSW, Australia (0061 2 9438 5040. <trevorsnotes@bigpond.com>. *P. L. World banknotes. Specialist in polymer notes.*

J. L. Williams

502 Clive Court, Maida Vale, London W9 1SG (020 7286 3461). *P. L. Wholesaler—dealers only.*

Barry Wright,

54 Dooley Drive, Bootle, Merseyside. L3O 8RT. *P. L. World banknotes.*

www.antiquestall.com

Online market place for banknotes and collectables.

Banks, Mints and numismatic
Bureaux
of the world

Many national banks and mints operate numismatic bureaux and sales agencies from which coins, notes and other numismatic products may be obtained direct. The conditions under which purchases may be made vary considerably. In many cases at the present time bureaux will accept orders from overseas customers quoting their credit card number and its expiry date; but in others payment can only be made by certified bank cheque, or international money order, or by girobank. Cash is seldom, if ever, acceptable. It is best to write in the first instance to enquire about methods of payment.

A

National Mint, Baghe Arg, Kabul, Afghanistan

Bank Mille Afghan, Kabul, Afghanistan

Banque d'Algerie, Sucursale d'Alger, 8 Boulevard Carnot, Alger, Algeria

Banco de Angola, Luanda, Daroal, Angola

Casa de Moneda de la Nacion, Avenida Antartica, Buenos Aires, BA, Argentina

Royal Australian Mint, Department of the Treasury, Canberra, ACT, Australia

GoldCorp Australia, Perth Mint Buildings, GPO Box M924, Perth, Western Australia 6001

Oesterreichsiches Hauptmunzamt, Am Heumarkt 1, A-1031 Wien, Postfach 225, Austria

Oesterreichische Nationalbank, A-1090 Wien, Otto Wagner-platz 3, Austria

B

Treasury Department, PO Box 557, Nassau, Bahamas (*coins*)

Ministry of Finance, PO Box 300, Nassau, Bahamas (*banknotes*)

Bank of Bahrain, PO Box 106, Manama, Bahrain

Eastern Bank, PO Box 29, Manama, Bahrain

Monnaie Royale de Belgique, Avenue de Pacheco 32, B-1000 Bruxelles, Belgium

Banque Nationale de Belgique SA, Caisse Centrale, Bruxelles, Belgium

Banque de Bruxelles SA, 2 Rue de la Regence, Bruxelles 1, Belgium

Casa de la Moneda, Potosi, Bolivia

Banco Central de Bolivia, La Paz, Bolivia

Casa da Moeda, Praca da Republica 173, Rio de Janeiro, Brazil

Hemus FTO, 7 Vasil Levski Street, Sofia C-1, Bulgaria

Banque de la Republique, Bujumbura, Burundi

C

Banque Centrale, Douala, Boite Postale 5.445, Cameroun

Royal Canadian Mint, 320 Sussex Drive, Ottawa 2, Ontario, Canada K1A 0G8

Casa de Moneda, Quinta Normal, Santiago, Chile

Casa de Moneda, Calle 11 no 4-93, Bogota, Colombia

Numismatic Section, The Treasury, Avarua, Rarotonga, Cook Islands

Banco Centrale de Costa Rica, Departamento de Contabilidad, San Jose, Costa Rica, CA

Central Bank of Cyprus, PO Box 1087, Nicosia, Cyprus

Artia, Ve Smekach 30, PO Box 790, Praha 1, Czech Republic

D

Den Kongelige Mønt, Amager Boulevard 115, København S, Denmark

Danmarks Nationalbank, Holmens Kanal 17, 1060 København K, Denmark

Banco Central de Santo Domingo, Santo Domingo, Dominican Republic

E

Banco Central, Quito, Ecuador

Mint House, Abbassia, Cairo, Egyptian Arab Republic

Exchange Control Department, National Bank of Egypt, Cairo, Egyptian Arab Republic

Banco Central de la Republica, Santa Isabel, Equatorial Guinea

Commercial Bank of Ethiopia, Foreign Branch, PO Box 255, Addis Ababa, Ethiopia

F

Currency Board, Victoria Parade, Suva, Fiji

Suomen Rahapaja, Katajanokanlaituri 3, Helsinki 16, Finland

Suomen Pankki, PO Box 10160, Helsinki 10, Finland

Hotel de Monnaie, 11 Quai de Conti, 75-Paris 6e, France

G

Banque Centrale Libreville, Boite Postale 112, Gabon

Verkaufstelle fur Sammlermunzen, D-638 Bad Homburg vdH, Bahnhofstrasse 16–18, Germany

Staatliche Munze Karlsruhe, Stephanienstrasse 28a, 75 Karlsruhe, Germany

Staatliche Munze Cannstatt, Taubenheimerstrasse

77, 7 Stuttgart-Bad, Germany

Bayerisches Hauptmunzamt, Hofgraben 4, 8 Munich, Germany

Hamburgische Munze, Norderstrasse 66, 2 Hamburg 1, Germany

Bank of Ghana, PO Box 2674, Accra, Ghana

Pobjoy Mint, Mint House, 92 Oldfields Road, Sutton, Surrey SM1 2NW

Royal Mint, Llantrisant, Mid Glamorgan, Wales, CF7 8YT

Royal Mint Coin Club, PO Box 500, Cardiff, CF1 1HA

Bank of Greece, Treasury Department, Cash, Delivery & Despatch Division, PO Box 105, Athens, Greece

Casa Nacional de Moneda, 6a Calle 4-28, Zona 1, Ciudad Guatemala, Republica de Guatemala CA

States Treasury, St Peter Port, Guernsey, Channel Islands

Bank of Guyana, PO Box 658, Georgetown, Guyana

H

Banque Nationale de la Republique d'Haiti, Rue Americaine et Rue Fereu, Port-au-Prince, Haiti

Banco Central de Honduras, Tegucigalpa DC, Honduras CA

State Mint, Ulloi utca 102, Budapest VIII, Hungary

Artex, PO Box 167, Budapest 62, Hungary

Magyar Nemzeti Bank, Board of Exchange, Budapest 54, Hungary

I

Sedlabanki Islands, Reykjavik, Iceland

Indian Government Mint, Bombay 1, India

Arthie Vasa, Keabajoran Baru, Djakarta, Indonesia

Perum Peruri, Djakarta, Indonesia

National Mint, Tehran, Iran

Bank Markazi Iran, Tehran, IranCentral Bank of Iraq, PO Box 64, Baghdad, Iraq

Central Bank of Ireland, Dublin 2, Republic of Ireland

The Treasury, Government Buildings, Prospect Hill, Douglas, Isle of Man

Israel Stamp and Coin Gallery, 4 Maze Street, Tel Aviv, Israel

Istituto Poligraphico e Zecca dello Stato, Via Principe Umberto, Roma, Italy

J

Decimal Currency Board, PO Box 8000, Kingston, Jamaica

Mint Bureau, 1 Shinkawasakicho, Kita-ku, Osaka 530, Japan

Numismatic Section, Treasury Department, St Helier, Jersey

Central Bank of Jordan, Amman, Jordan

Banque Nationale du Liban, Rue Masraf Loubnan, Beirut, Lebanon

K

Central Bank, PO Box 526, Kuwait

L

Bank of Lithuania, Cash Department, Gedimino av. 6, 2001 Vilius, Lithuania

Caisse Generale de l'Etat, 5 Rue Goethe, Luxembourg-Ville, Grande Duche de Luxembourg

M

Institut d'Emission Malgache, Boite Postale 205, Tananarive, Madagascar

Central Bank of Malta, Valletta 1, Malta

Casa de Moneda, Calle del Apartado no 13, Mexico 1, DF, Mexico

Le Tresorier General des Finances, Monte Carlo, Principaute de Monaco

Banque de l'Etat du Maroc, Rabat, Morocco

Banco Nacional Ultramarino, Maputo, Republica de Mocambique

British Bank of the Middle East, Muscat

N

Royal Mint, Dharahara, Katmandu, Nepal

Nepal Rastra Bank, Katmandu, Nepal

Rijks Munt, Leidseweg 90, Utrecht, Netherlands

Hollandsche Bank-Unie NV, Willemstad, Breedestraat 1, Curacao, Netherlands Antilles

Central Bank of Curacao, Willemstad, Curacao, Netherlands Antilles

The Treasury, Private Bag, Lambton Quay, Wellington, New Zealand

Banco de Nicaragua, Departamento de Emison, La Tresoria, Apartada 2252, Managua, Nicaragua

Nigerian Security Printing and Minting Corporation, Ahmadu Bello Road, Victoria Island, Lagos, Nigeria

Central Bank of Nigeria, Tinubu Square LB, Lagos, Nigeria

Norges Bank, Oslo, Norway

Den Kongelige Mynt, Hyttegaten, Konigsberg, Norway

P

Pakistan State Mint, Baghban Pura, Lahore 9, Pakistan

National Development Bank, Asuncion, Paraguay

Casa Nacional de Moneda, Calle Junin 791, Lima, Peru

Central Bank of the Philippines, Manila, Philippines

Bank Handlowy w Warszawie, Ul. Romuald Traugutta 7, Warsaw, Poland

Desa Foreign Trade Department, Al. Jerozolimskie 2, Warszawa, Poland

Casa da Moeda, Avenida Dr Antonio Jose de Almeida, Lisbon 1, Portugal

R

Cartimex, 14-18 Aristide Briand St, PO Box 134-135, Bucharest, Roumania

Bank of Foreign Trade, Commercial Department, Moscow K 16, Neglinnaja 12, Russian Federation

Banque Nationale du Rwanda, Boite Postale 351, Kigali, Republique Rwandaise

S

Numismatic Section, Box 194, GPO, Apia, Samoa

Azienda Autonoma di Stato Filatelica-Numismatica, Casalla Postale 1, 47031 Repubblica di San Marino

Banque Internationale pour le Commerce, 2 Avenue Roume, Dakar, Senegal

Bank of Yugoslavia, PO Box 1010, Belgrade, Serbia

The Treasury, PO Box 59, Victoria, Seychelles

Bank of Sierra Leone, PO Box 30, Freetown, Sierra Leone

The Singapore Mint, 249 Jalan Boon Lay, Jurong, Singapore

South African Mint, PO Box 464, Pretoria, South Africa

Government Printing Agency, 93 Bukchang Dong, Chungku, Seoul, Republic of South Korea

Fabrica Nacional de Moneda y Timbre, Jorge Juan 106, Madrid 9, Spain

Bank of Sri Lanka, PO Box 241, Colombo, Sri Lanka

Hong Kong and Shanghai Banking Corporation, PO Box 73, Colombo 1, Sri Lanka

Sudan Mint, PO Box 43, Khartoum, Sudan

Bank of Sudan, PO Box 313, Khartoum, Sudan

Bank of Paramaribo, Paramaribo, Suriname

Kungelige Mynt och Justeringsverket, Box 22055, Stockholm 22, Sweden

Eidgenossische Staatskasse, Bundesgasse 14, CH-3003, Berne, Switzerland

Central Bank of Syria, Damascus, Syrian Arab Republic

T

Central Mint of China, 44 Chiu Chuan Street, Taipei, Taiwan, ROC

Royal Thai Mint, 4 Chao Fah Road, Bangkok, Thailand

Numismatic Section, The Treasury, Nuku'alofa, Tonga

Central Bank of Trinidad and Tobago, PO Box 1250, Port of Spain, Trinidad

Banque Centrale de Tunisie, Tunis, Tunisia

State Mint, Maliye Bakanligi Darphane Mudurlugu, Istanbul, Turkey

U

Bank of Uganda, PO Box 7120, Kampala, Uganda

Numismatic Service, US Assay Office, 350 Duboce Avenue, San Francisco, CA, 94102, USA

Office of the Director of the Mint, Treasury Department, Washington, DC, 20220, USA

Philadelphia Mint, 16th and Spring Garden Streets, Philadelphia, PA, 19130, USA

Franklin Mint, Franklin Center, Pennsylvania, 19063, USA

Banco Central del Uruguay, Cerrito 351, Montevideo, RO del Uruguay

V

Ufficio Numismatico, Governatorato dello Stato della Citta de Vaticano, Italy

Banco Central de Venezuela, Caracas, Venezuela

Y

Yemen Bank, Sana'a, Yemen.

Z

Bank of Zambia, PO Box 80, Lusaka, Zambia

Chief Cashier, Reserve Bank, PO Box 1283, Harare, Zimbabwe

Bank of England, 1845—the Five Pound Bank Note Office.

Banknotes and
The law

Counterfeit Currency

A counterfeit is a forgery or imitation of a coin or banknote produced with the intention of defrauding the revenue of the State or deceiving members of the public. By the Coinage Offences Act (1861) it was a felony to counterfeit gold or silver coins. Lesser offences included the gilding of farthings and sixpences to pass them off as half-sovereigns, the possession of moulds, machines or tools clandestinely removed from the Royal Mint, the impairment or diminution of gold or silver coins by filing or clipping (or even the possession of such filings and clippings).

The Coinage Act of 1870 made provision for the counterfeiting of base-metal coins, or the stamping of letters or words on coins of any kind, or the forging of colonial coinage. The most celebrated prosecution under this Act occurred in 1930 when Martin Coles Harman was convicted and fined £5 for issuing bronze coins resembling the British penny and halfpenny for the island of Lundy of which he was then the proprietor. Interestingly, no attempt was made to prosecute the Birmingham Mint which actually struck the coins (prudently omitting the H mintmark).

The making of medals or coins resembling current coin became a misdemeanour under the Counterfeit Medal Act of 1883. This Act is invoked from time to time against manufacturers or distributors of medallic pieces or coin jewellery. Such pieces, often struck in 9 carat gold, are deemed to infringe the Act if, for example, they have a figure even vaguely resembling St George and the Dragon on one side. The use of the royal effigy, however, without due authorisation, is regarded as a misdemeanour punishable by an unlimited fine and the confiscation of tools, dies and instruments. At the present time it is a serious offence to make a counterfeit of a currency note or coin with the intention of passing it off or tendering it as genuine. This offence carries a maximum penalty of ten years' imprisonment or an unlimited fine, or both. Making a counterfeit of a currency note or coin without lawful authority incurs a penalty up to two years' imprisonment or an unlimited fine, or both.

Passing or tendering as genuine anything which is known or believed to be a counterfeit of a currency note or coin renders the criminal on conviction to a term of ten years' imprisonment or an unlimited fine, or both. The mere possession of any forged note or coin is itself a criminal offence. Possessing countertfeits without authority or permission so to do, and doing so knowingly, renders the possessor liable to two years' imprisonment or an unlimited fine, or both. The Act also stipulates that the reproduction of a current banknote—of the Bank of England or of the Scottish and Northern Irish banks is a serious offence. This clause covers even such apparently innocent acts as making a photocopy (whether in black and white or full colour) of a current banknote, the photography of such a note or the illustration of such a note in any book, magazine or newspaper. Strict regulations are laid down concerning the legitimate illustration of notes, whether current or not, in books and periodicals; such illustrations must be either greatly reduced or enlarged *and* must bear a prominent defacement, such as SPECIMEN or CANCELLED. It is also a serious offence to utilise a reproduction of a current British banknote in any medium. Theoretically this includes such things as tea-towels, T-shirts, mugs, plates and other souvenirs in glass or ceramics, but in practice the law seems to turn a blind eye to such practices. Imitations and parodies of notes and coins are also regarded as infringements of the law, but in these instances prosecution of the offender seldom proceeds; a warning is generally regarded as sufficient, provided that the offending article or articles are withdrawn and suppressed.

The advent of high-definition colour photo-copying in recent years has brought the offence of reproduction into prominence once more. The regulations have been tightened considerably and there have been several cases of successful prosecution. In each case, however, the intent deliberately to deceive the public by passing a colour photocopy as a genuine note was proved. Technically the offence takes places as soon as the photocopy is made, for whatever purpose, but as a rule only those cases in which an element of fraudulent deception subsequently arose were pursued with the full rigour of the law. The law is quite clear, however, and it is a criminal offence to make a colour photocopy or photograph of any current British note unless permission to do so has been obtained from the Treasury. The maximum penalty on conviction is an unlimited fine.

The note-issuing banks have, of course, taken steps in recent years to incorporate further security devices into their notes, notably the use of latent images and underprints in colours which are difficult, if not impossible to photocopy accurately. At the same time, the adoption of metal strips and more complex watermark devices has theoretically made the task of the forger much more difficult. If, by some unlucky chance, someone passes a dud note on to you, you must make no attempt to pass it in turn. To do so renders you liable to prosecution for uttering a forgery. Forged notes must be handed over to the police as soon as possible. If you receive a forged note in payment for goods or services you are entitled to claim its face value from the person who gave it to you. Even if the person giving you the note did not realise that it was counterfeit, it is assumed in law that he or she represented to you that the note was worth its face value at the time the note was passed. If the tenderer knew that the note was forged, he can be prosecuted; but at the end of the day he is still liable to you for the fraud and can be sued in the civil courts for the recovery of the sum involved. If, on the other hand, you received the money as a gift, you have no legal claim against the person who gave it to you. If you pay someone with a counterfeit note or coin unknowingly, you have committed no offence, but you must pay again. The degree of culpability is often difficult to prove or disprove, but it is unlikely that a prosecution would be initiated on the basis of a single note or a solitary coin.

Legal Tender

The dictionary defines this as currency which a creditor is bound by law to accept as payment of a money debt. Debts and purchases must be paid for in cash of legal tender unless the creditor or seller is willing to accept payment in another form, such as a postal order, money order, cheque or, nowadays, credit card. Bank of England notes of any denomination are legal tender in England and Wales. Formerly Bank of England pound notes (but no other) were legal tender in Scotland. Technically, since the demise of the pound note, no Bank of England notes are legal tender in Scotland, although in practice they circulate freely north of the Border. Even more surprisingly, Scottish banknotes are not legal tender anywhere, not even in Scotland! The subtle difference is reflected in the actual wording of the promise on English and Scottish banknotes. Thus English notes are inscribed "I promise to pay the bearer on demand the sum of . . ." without stipulating any specific place, the promise being made by the Chief Cashier. Scottish notes, on the other hand, have the promise in the third person. It is the bank itself which makes the promise "to pay the bearer on demand . . . pounds sterling at their head office here in Edinburgh, by order of the Board". In practice, however, Scottish banknotes are accepted without question, not only throughout Scotland but also in parts of England, and are generally accepted in London, although there is no obligation on the part of a creditor so to do.

Apart from gold coins, the base-metal pound coin is legal tender for payment of any amounts. So, too, presumably, are the various two-pound and five-pound base-metal coins of recent years, even though they have been struck as commemoratives and not intended for general circulation in the ordinary sense. Smaller denominations are only legal tender up to a maximum value in each case. In the case of 50p coins, 25p crowns and 20p coins, they may be used alone, or in combination with each other, in payment of amounts up to £10. 10p and 5p coins, alone or in combination, may be used for sums up to £5. Bronze 1p and 2p coins, however, can only be used for payment of amounts up to 20p. In practice, of course, you can probably get away with making payment in larger quantities (within reason!) although strictly speaking there is no obligation on the part of your creditor to accept them.

Value Added Tax

This is a matter which primarily concerns dealers, but it also applies to those who dabble in coins on a part-time basis, and has implications for collectors at all levels. Briefly, anyone conducting a business, or in self-employment, who has a turnover in excess of £43,000 per annum, must register with HM Customs and Excise for the collection and payment of Value Added Tax. Anyone whose turnover is less than £43,000 is exempt from the obligation to register, but is at liberty to register if he or she feels that this would be advantageous. It is nice to think that there is an element of choice in this, although one would be hard pressed to think why anyone would voluntarily register for VAT unless they absolutely had to! Incidentally, the government raised the VAT registration level by 40 per cent to £35,000 in March 1991 with the avowed intention of relieving a large number of businesses from this burden, at a time when the rate of tax was increased from 15 per cent to 17.5 per cent. Assuming that you are a dealer with a turnover above the magic limit, then you are committing a serious offence if you fail to register. Registration then lays you open to the full machinery of the system. You have to charge VAT on all goods and services, issuing VAT invoices and receipts and keeping detailed accounts which are liable to snap inspection at any time. You have to make quarterly returns to Customs and Excise of the amount of tax you have collected. From this you are allowed to deduct the VAT which you yourself have paid out in the course of your business, and you then have to remit the difference to the VAT collector. Of course, should the amount you have paid exceed the tax you have collected, you receive a repayment in due course. This arises in businesses which handle zero-rated goods and services, but coins and medals do not come within that category.

From January 1, 1995 the special margin scheme of accounting for VAT currently available for certain second-hand goods, such as cars, was extended to almost all second-hand goods. The scheme allows businesses buying and selling eligible goods to account for VAT only on the difference between the buying and selling prices of these items.

A special system of accounting has recently been introduced which enables some dealers to account for VAT without the need to keep a detailed record of every transaction. Certain works of art, antiques and collector's items, including "secondhand" coins, defined in Notice 712 *Second-hand goods*, were exempt from VAT at import. From January 1, 1996 these items became subject to VAT at import at an effective rate of 2.5 per cent.

Importing Coins by Mail

Elsewhere in this volume will be found the names and addresses of mints, banks and numismatic bureaux around the world from whom it may be possible to obtain currency direct. It is a wise precaution to write to these bodies in the first instance for details of their sales and distribution. In some cases they appoint a dealer in Britain as an agent and this is a method of purchase that removes a great deal of the hassle and red tape. Nowadays, however, many mints and banks are quite happy to use the credit card system to make it easy to part you from your money. The problem arises, however, when the notes are despatched. As a rule, banks and mints stipulate quite clearly that they will not accept orders prepaid in cash, and it is an offence to send coins or banknotes out of the country as payment, except through banks authorised for this purpose. Cheques drawn on British banks should not be used. Indeed, this may be actively discouraged by the imposition of heavy clearance and handling charges at the other end. The converse is also true, although Americans seem to think that dollar cheques drawn on some obscure mid-West bank will be eagerly accepted here, and are consequently aggrieved when it is tactfully pointed out to them that this creates enormous problems— to say nothing of the swingeing bank charges incurred in converting such cheques to sterling. Other than credit cards, the Girobank system is probably the best method of remitting currency from one country to another; full details may be obtained from any post office. Details on the preferred method of sending remittances, or transferring cash to another country, as well as the transmission of coins by post to different countries, will be found in the *Royal Mail International Service Guide*.

The receipt of postal packets containing banknotes from abroad makes you liable for Value Added Tax on their importation. As a rule, the despatching mint or bank will have affixed a Customs declaration to the packet, listing the contents, their weight and value, and it is on that basis that VAT will be calculated. The position regarding the import and export of coins by post is more complicated, and applies also to goods sent on approval. In such cases you must consult your Customs and Excise office who will advise you on the correct procedure and what your liabilities will be to tax in either case. This also applies to dealers taking stock out of the country to a show and then re-importing the unsold stock afterwards, or importing material purchased at the show.

Buying and Selling

When goods are sold, the seller and the buyer enter into a contract which confers rights on and imposes obligations on both parties. The contract need not be in writing. There is no law governing the quality of goods sold by a private individual. If you purchase a coin from a fellow-collector as a result of an informal meeting at the local numismatic society it is incumbent on you to ensure that what you buy is what you think you are buying. If you purchase something from a dealer or shopkeeper, however, you are entitled under the Sale of Goods Act to goods of "merchantable quality" which means that they must be reasonably fit for their purpose. Items sold under a specific description, on the other hand, must correspond exactly with that description. If they do not, the seller *even a private individual* can be sued under the Sale of Goods Act. This is an important distinction because there is an erroneous notion that the Act does not apply to transactions between private individuals. If A sells a coin to B, purporting it to be a rare date, and B subsequently discovers that the date has been deliberately altered, then B can sue A. Even if A claims that he made the sale in good faith, believing the coin to be a genuine rare date, he will still be liable for restitution (giving B his money back) and may also face a claim for damages. The Sale of Goods Act thus overturns the traditional adage *caveat emptor* which, in its full formula, translates as "let the buyer beware for he ought not to be ignorant of the nature of the property which he is buying from another party". Traditionally this was the maxim applicable at auctions. Once the auctioneer's gavel had dropped, the successful bidder had, in effect, made a contract with the vendor and was bound to pay for the lot, even if he subsequently discovered that what he had purchased was not what he had imagined. The view was that it was up to the purchaser to ensure beforehand that what he purchased was genuine and answered the description in the sale catalogue.

Because of vexatious disputes arising from questions of authenticity, and with the Sale of Goods Act breathing down their necks, many auctioneers now have a safety net, in the form of extensions. These enable successful bidders to delay payment for two or three weeks while they seek expertisation of doubtful material. In other words, the law allows a cooling-off period, but only for he legitimate purpose of verifying the authenticity of items over which there may be some doubt. This is only operative in cases where a coin or medal is sold as genuine, and described and estimated in value accordingly. In many doubtful cases, however, an auctioneer will cover himself by adding the crucial words "as is" to the description of a lot. Then, indeed, it is a case of *caveat emptor*. The auctioneer has done everything humanly possible to draw attention to the controversial nature of the item, and it must then rest on the judgment of the purchaser.

On the subject of auctions there are legal aspects

which are not always apparent, as well as subtle differences in law and practice between England and Scotland. These tend to arise in cases where coins and medals come up for sale at provincial general mixed auctions, rather than in the sales conducted by numismatic auctioneers. Goods up for auction may be subject to an upset price which is made public as the price at which the bidding will start. A reserve price, on the other hand, is known only to the auctioneer, and if it is not reached, the goods will not be sold. Upset prices are common in Scotland, reserve prices in England. If no upset price is specified and the goods are not subject to a reserve price then the highest bid secures them, even though it may not be as high as the vendor hoped for. If a seller notifies other bidders that he is bidding for his own goods, or that he has employed an agent to bid for him, the bidding is legal. If he does not give notice and bids himself, or gets someone to bid for him, thus forcing up the price, the sale is fraudulent, and the buyer can purchase the goods for the amount of the last bid he made before fraudulent bidding started.

One frequently hears dark, but usually apocryphal, tales of "the ring" in action to depress the bidding and secure items below the price commensurate with their actual value. This is a fraudulent practice and in law is regarded as a criminal conspiracy. In practice, however, it would be very difficult for a group of dealers or other individuals to keep the bidding down merely by sitting on their hands. This practice could only operate successfully in sales which were largely, if not entirely, frequented by dealers. But coin sales, like other specialist collector-orientated auctions, are characterised by a high proportion of private bidders in attendance. Any conspiracy by a ring would merely allow some private bidder to step in and secure the lot at a bargain price. Rings are illegal, but in practice prosecutions are very rare as it is extremely difficult to obtain proof of their operations. What is more likely to happen is that dealers have been known to act in concert to force up the bidding to frighten off some unwelcome interloper. Here again, such tales are legion, but astonishingly lacking in specific details. The golden rule in attending auctions is to know what you are going after, and to have a pretty precise idea of how much you are prepared to pay. Do not be stampeded in the heat of the moment into going way beyond your limit.

Taxation of Profits on Disposal

The Inland Revenue define an asset as "any form of property (other than sterling) wherever situated". A disposal includes a sale, exchange or gift of an asset, or the receipt of a capital sum in respect of them. In layman's terms you dispose of an asset when you sell it, give it away, exchange it or lose it. A transfer of assets between husband and wife doesn't count (unless they are legally separated), nor does the transfer of an asset you leave when you die. If a disposal results in a profit you could be liable to tax. Any profit made on the sale of certain assets, including coins, medals and other collectables, constitutes a capital gain and is subject to Capital Gains Tax (CGT) which is now charged at the same 25% and 40% rates as income tax. However the government allows you to make a total capital gain in the current tax year of £5,500 before tax becomes chargeable. If this is the case, and the total proceeds from disposal do not exceed £10,000, then a simple declaration to this effect is all you need to make in the relevant section of your annual tax return.

Computing the actual capital gain is a complicated matter. Suppose you purchased a banknote in 1960 for £5,000 and sold it in 1993 for £12,000. On the face of it, you've made a capital gain of £7,000 and you might think that you were liable to CGT because the gain was over £5,500. However, the *length of time* you've held the asset also has to be taken into consideration. From April 6, 1988 the law was altered so that only gains made after March 31, 1982 are now taxable. In effect, you are taxed as if you acquired the coin on March 31, 1982. The initial value of the coin is deemed to be its market value at that date. If the gain from March 1982 to the time of disposal is greater than the overall gain from acquisition in 1960 to disposal in 1993, you take the lesser of the two figures. If this produces a gain, whereas the old method of working it out would have produced a loss, you will be regarded, for tax purposes, as having made neither a gain nor a loss on disposal. You have a choice of opting for computing from the time of actual acquisition or from March 1982, whichever seems the more advantageous; but once you've made your choice you cannot subsequently change your mind.

How do you establish what the coin was worth in March 1982? The Inland Revenue tend to regard Seaby, Krause or other relevant catalogues as their yardstick. The difference between the nominal or catalogue value in 1982 and what you eventually got for the coin *assuming that the latter was greater,* might be regarded as the capital gain, but even then the position is complicated by inflation in the intervening years eroding the real value of the coin.

At this stage things get really complicated as you have to work out the indexation allowance. This is determined by the Retail Prices Index (RPI), and you need to know the RPI for (a) the month of disposal, and (b) the month in which you acquired the asset, or March 1982, if later. The RPI is announced each month by the Departmenrt of Employment and is published in its *Employment Gazette* which ought to be available in your local public library. Take the RPI for the month of the disposal and subtract the RPI for the month when indexation commenced. Then divide the result by the RPI for the month when indexation began, and work out this figure to the nearest third decimal place. This is known as the indexation factor, which you then multiply by the initial value of your coin. Simple isn't it? In most cases, however, I expect you will have made a capital loss in real terms, so these sums, though necessary to satisfy the Inland Revenue, are largely academic.

NOTES